sex research
new developments

CONTRIBUTORS

FRANK A. BEACH, Professor of Psychology, University of California, Berkeley

ROBERT W. GOY, Associate Scientist, Oregon Regional Primate Research Center

HARRY F. HARLOW, Professor of Psychology and Director, University of Wisconsin Primate Laboratory and Wisconsin Regional Primate Research Center, The University of Wisconsin

MARGARET K. HARLOW, Research Associate, University of Wisconsin Primate Laboratory and Wisconsin Regional Primate Research Center, The University of Wisconsin

EVELYN HOOKER, Research Associate in Psychology, University of California, Los Angeles

VIRGINIA E. JOHNSON, Research Associate, Reproductive Biology Research Foundation, St. Louis

PAUL D. MACLEAN, Chief, Section on Limbic Integration and Behavior, Laboratory of Neurophysiology, Clinical Center, National Institutes of Health

ABRAHAM H. MASLOW, Professor of Psychology, Brandeis University.

WILLIAM H. MASTERS, Research Director, Reproductive Biology Research Foundation, St. Louis

JOHN MONEY, Associate Professor of Medical Psychology and Pediatrics, The Johns Hopkins University School of Medicine

VINCENT NOWLIS, Professor of Psychology, University of Rochester

DONALD W. PFAFF, Psychology Department, Massachusetts Institute of Technology

CHARLES H. PHOENIX, Associate Scientist, Oregon Regional Primate Research Center

WILLIAM C. YOUNG, Director, Oregon Regional Primate Research Center

NEW YORK • CHICAGO • SAN FRANCISCO • TORONTO • LONDON

sex research
new developments

edited by **JOHN MONEY**
Departments of Psychiatry and Pediatrics
The Johns Hopkins University

Sponsored by the New England Psychological Association

HOLT, RINEHART AND WINSTON   *1965*

ACKNOWLEDGMENTS

Permissions to republish are gratefully acknowledged as follows:

American Association for the Advancement of Science, for W. C. Young, R. W. Roy, and C. H. Phoenix, Hormones and sexual behavior. *Science, 143,* 212–218, 1964. (Copyright 1964 by the American Association for the Advancement of Science.)

The Menninger Foundation, for H. F. Harlow and Margaret K. Harlow, The effect of rearing conditions on behavior. *Bulletin of the Menninger Clinic, 26,* 213–224, 1962.

Western Journal of Surgery Publishing Company, for W. H. Masters, The sexual response cycle of the human female: I. Gross anatomic considerations. *Western Journal of Surgery, Obstetrics and Gynecology, 68,* 57–72, 1960. W. H. Masters and Virginia E. Johnson, The sexual response cycle of the human female: III. The clitoris: anatomic and clinical considerations. *Western Journal of Surgery, Obstetrics and Gynecology, 70,* 248–257, 1962. (Both these articles have been updated by the authors.)

The Williams and Wilkins Company, for P. D. MacLean, New findings relevant to the evolution of the psychosexual functions of the brain. *Journal of Nervous and Mental Disease, 135,* 289–301, 1962.

FOREWORD

This monograph is the outgrowth of an all-day symposium held at the third annual meeting of the New England Psychological Association in Boston, November 9, 1963. We hope that it will be the first in a series of such symposia. One of the aims of our organization has been to encourage the exchange of scientific ideas among workers in a variety of disciplines that are relevant to psychology but not necessarily within its confines. At a time when scientific societies have tended to become increasingly devoted to special subfields, when the areas of study are progressively fragmented, and when papers at meetings are becoming shorter, of necessity more cryptic and directed to audiences of sub- (or perhaps super-) specialists, we have as our purpose the bridging of the narrow compartmentalization of knowledge. To this end we instituted invitational programs where adequate time is allowed for speakers to present systematic points of view as well as for meaningful subsequent discussion. The meetings are held at least in part with no conflicting programs and a concerted effort is made to have material presented that, while relevant and interesting to psychologists, will be novel to most of the audience because it encompasses work in fields outside of psychology proper.

Some years ago, when it appeared that many new discoveries came at points where disciplines crossed and merged, interdisciplinary collaboration became fashionable. While collaboration for its own sake alone has proven to be a will-o'-the-wisp, the basic reason for its original enthusiastic reception remains. It appears to us that a number of conditions need to exist before an interdisciplinary approach becomes meaningful. It is necessary that (1) the participants share interest in a specific phenomenon; (2) their work be empirical in nature; (3) the research in each field be sufficiently advanced; and (4) the investigators recognize the relevance of work in other disciplines. When these conditions appear to be met, then an interdisciplinary symposium becomes an exciting and rewarding experience—certainly for the listeners and hopefully for the participants.

We were exceedingly fortunate in obtaining the cooperation of a distinguished panel of visitors who willingly gave their time and effort to make this symposium possible. The original participants were limited by distance, time, and funds. They were chosen to represent a variety of empirical approaches to an understanding of the sexual role.

Dr. John Money, whose pioneering work on the systematic study of "nature's mistakes" has challenged many time-honored beliefs about sexual identity, discussed both his own work and that of his colleagues. In his contribution, he has brought together a large body of data on the biological determination of sex and its remarkable lack of correlation with the psychological attributes commonly identified with it.

Dr. Evelyn Hooker has approached an understanding of sexual identity through an almost naturalistic study of socially adequately functioning homosexuals. Her methods of study combine the best techniques available to the anthropologist on the one hand and the clinical psychologist on the other. Her studies have been unique in many respects. Certainly it is the only major investigation of any sizable group of individuals that has been followed over a period of several years without the loss of a single subject. The data obtained have been particularly vital since the group under investigation does not normally come to the attention of trained workers. They are individuals who would not present themselves as patients and,

except for the fact of their homosexuality, are functioning remarkably well.

Dr. William Masters, working as a research gynecologist,
was able to present psychophysiological data about the mechanism of orgasm and some of its implications that would not be
possible to obtain except with medical sanction. His systematic
inquiry into a topic that in the past has substituted speculation,
dogmatic assertion, hearsay, and limited personal experience
for genuine and complete data has provided information of
great importance, both theoretically and clinically.

Professor Frank Beach, summing up his own extensive
studies as well as the work of students and colleagues, used the
approach of the comparative psychologist in the study of sexual
behavior in animals. Both the consistencies and the incon-
sistencies of sexual behavior across species are indeed startling.
These studies help to provide a meaningful, broader, biological
context for the other papers dealing primarily with human
research.

The symposium papers were discussed by Professors
Vincent Nowlis and Abrahom Maslow. Professor Nowlis was
able to contribute from his experience, both in the study of
sexual behavior while working with Kinsey and in his own
more recent empirical research on the study of mood. Professor
Maslow, whose early work included studies of sexual behavior
in monkeys, from his enduring interest in dynamic psychology
helped to provide critical balance by emphasizing some of
the humanistic issues involved in the scientific study of sexual
behavior.

Professor Jerome Bruner chaired the symposium, ably
managing to allow the generation of an amount of heat sufficient to provide excitement but not to obscure the discussion.

This monograph was made possible by Dr. John Money's
willingness to edit the original symposium and to add contributions from several colleagues who were represented indirectly,
through reference to their work, in the symposium but were
not able, for one reason or another, to participate. The monograph has, therefore, been expanded to include reviews of
much of the empirical work that helped to provide the background that has made this symposium meaningful. These stud-

ies are Dr. Harry Harlow's investigation of social and sexual behavior in monkeys, Dr. Paul MacLean's work on the identification of cerebral sexual centers, the endocrinological studies of Drs. William Young, Robert Goy, and Charles Phoenix, as well as an extensive summary of recent findings in neurohormonal research on sexual behavior by Dr. Donald Pfaff.

Speaking for the program committee of the New England Psychological Association, we would like to take this opportunity to thank Dr. Money, the contributors, and the publishers for making the first NEPA monograph a reality.

MARTIN T. ORNE

LEWIS B. KLEBANOFF

PREFACE

This book is preponderantly attentive to what may be broadly construed as the psychophysiology of sex, since it aims to reflect the most significant developments in sex research during the last ten years or so. In an earlier era, psychodynamic explanations captured enthusiasm and prompted research. But psychodynamics did not follow through with the promised payoff in terms of scientific prediction and control of sexual development and pathology. Obviously other contributing factors need to be investigated, and new sophistications of theory achieved.

The old theoretical dichotomy between the physical and the psychological now no longer holds in sex research. For one thing, the new genetics teaches clearly that heredity and environment are not truly juxtaposable, for the genotype, in order to translate itself into the phenotype, needs an optimal and specifiable environment. Exposure to an adverse environment may alter or deflect the norm of reaction.

It is the new concept of critical periods of development, however, that has done most to render archaic the dichotomy between physical and psychological. Critical-period phenomena demonstrate clearly that development and differentiation may be responsive and adaptive to environmental stimuli during a phylogenetically limited critical period, and then become relatively fixed and immutable, and built into the system.

There is no intractable antagonism between psychodynamics or sociodynamics on the one hand, and physiodynamics on the other. One suspects that the developments in sex research yet to come will show the way to their increasing synthesis, and perhaps provide the New England Psychological Association with the occasion to be again a gracious host to a symposium on sex.

The participants of the first symposium are represented in Part I of this volume, in the order of their participation. The chapters were prepared for the occasion, and subsequently revised for publication, except in the case of Dr. Masters who elected to update and republish material already prepared in collaboration with Virginia Johnson. Dr. Maslow's chapter follows closely the tape transcript and has, more than the others, the flavor of oral delivery.

Part II presents an anthology of four review articles. Three of them are reproduced with permission, namely those by Paul MacLean, William C. Young, and Harry Harlow. Donald Pfaff's review is here published for the first time. Between them and in conjunction with Part I, these four papers bring the reader effectively up to date with contemporary developments in sex research and theory.

Mrs. Beverly Schmidt has earned special commendation for expert attention to typing and editing the manuscript and preparing the glossary.

J.M.

BALTIMORE, MARYLAND
1965

CONTENTS

part one

between the "invert, or passive male homoerotic," who "feels himself to be a woman, and this not only in genital inter-course, but in all relations of life," and the "active homo-sexual," who "feels himself a man in every respect. . . . The object of his inclination alone is exchanged. . . ." (p. 300). Terman and Miles (1936) employed this distinction between the "passive male homosexual, or invert" and the "active, or masculine" homosexual, as defined by sexual practice, with results that tended to confirm the psychological gender (M–F) differences between the two types. Brown (1958, 1961) has reviewed the use of the concepts of inversion and homo-sexuality. He suggests that the term "sexual inversion" be applied to those individuals who have an "identification with, preference for, and adoption of the sex role of the other sex . . ." (1961, p. 1018). The term "homosexual" should then be used to refer to individuals who seek sexual satisfaction predomi-nantly with members of their own sex. He asserts that "inversion is only *one* condition that may be related to *one* form of homo-sexuality." "*Passive, feminine* male homosexuality and *active, masculine* female homosexuality will often be found among male and female inverts respectively" (1961, p. 1019).

A number of writers, including Brown (1958), Terman and Miles (1936), and Rado (1949), while emphasizing the active–passive dichotomy in sexual patterns and the corre-sponding masculine–feminine dichotomy in gender identity in some individuals, have noted that the patterns of many homo-sexuals cannot be characterized by such dichotomous concepts, but represent variable combinations or intermediate grades. Recently, Westwood (1960), Bieber, Dain, Dince, Drellich, Grand, Gundlach, Kremer, Rifkin, Wilbur, and Bieber (1962), and Hooker (1961) have questioned the accuracy of the terms "active" and "passive," when used to describe homosexual acts, and, either explicitly or by implication, have questioned the long-accepted gender role connotations of these terms.

The perspective of the two-sexed heterosexual society has dominated all attempts to classify the patterned relation-

---

described, should be restricted to *typical sexual performance*. The gender (M–F) connotations of these performances need not then be implicitly assumed.

ships between sexual performance and psychological gender in male homosexuals. Many male homosexuals, however, who develop working solutions to the problems with which they are confronted by virtue of their sexual object-choice, live in two worlds, the larger society and homosexual subcultures that are, in the main, one-sexed societies. I propose that, in the context of their subcultures in relation to the larger society, homosexuals develop working solutions to problems of sexual performance and psychological gender which cannot be understood in the perspective of the two-sexed heterosexual world.

Is there a relation between what male homosexuals do sexually and how they feel about themselves as men? Is it possible for the male homosexual to "feel himself a man in every respect," not only in sexual activity but in his work life, erotic fantasies, social relations with nonhomosexual males, and in his domestic activities and love relationships? Does the status of being a male homosexual in our society inevitably produce problems about masculinity in a man who identifies himself as one? What is the influence on sexual patterns and a conscious sense of being masculine or feminine, of the fact that many male homosexuals participate in some sector of the homosexual subculture? If identity is discovered in interaction with others and is therefore not fixed and immutable but changes over time—a thesis which Strauss (1959) and others have developed—what transformations of psychosexual identity occur with progressive involvement in the homesexual way of life? These questions suggest an expanded frame of reference, within which some of the problems of the psychosexual identities of male homosexuals will be examined.

RESEARCH SUBJECTS AND METHOD

The primary data have been obtained from thirty men, about whom I have previously reported other research findings (1957, 1958). They are adult homosexual males who are erotically and emotionally attracted to, and engage in overt sexual behavior exclusively or predominantly with, other males.[2]

---

[2] At the time these subjects were first interviewed in 1954, all but three of the thirty were exclusively homosexual, and these three had had a

Detailed accounts of how they were obtained as research subjects, and of the criteria used in their selection, have already been reported; therefore only a brief summary will be given here. They were obtained by gaining access to homosexual groups and networks of friends, and by establishing a viable research role with them as one who was completely trustworthy and morally nonjudgmental. They were originally selected as "normal"; that is, they were not seeking psychological help, were gainfully employed, and, in an initial screening interview, showed no gross signs of psychological disturbance. To assess the kind and degree of normality or psychopathology is one of the objectives of the research.

They were committed to homosexuality, albeit with varying degrees of acceptance of that status. I use the term *committed* here to refer to the fact that they rejected the possibility of a change in sexual pattern to that of heterosexuality and, in most instances, did not see such a change as being desirable—although some expressed the opinion that if change were possible and could have occurred before they had adjusted to a homosexual way of life, they would have preferred it. As already indicated, they were erotically and emotionally attracted to, and engaged in overt sexual behavior predominantly or exclusively with, other males. I first interviewed them and administered a battery of psychological tests in 1954,[3] and have re-interviewed them twice since, the last time in 1962. Some of them have been interviewed at much more frequent intervals.

The complete and generous cooperation of these thirty men over a period of eight years—which continues at the present time—thus made possible a 100 percent follow-up. Most follow-up studies report a sizable loss of subjects over time. Some comments by way of explanation of the long-sustained motivation of these men to cooperate with the research may

---

maximum of three overt heterosexual experiences each. On the Kinsey scale, twenty-seven would be rated as 6, and these three would be rated as 5. All of them identified themselves as homosexual in their patterns of desire and behavior.

[3] When first interviewed in 1954, the age range was 25–57, with a mean age of 34.5.

be appropriate. Their cooperation was completely voluntary, since they were not paid. For some individuals, the primary motivation was to make a contribution to a scientific inquiry into homosexuality. Having read a good deal of the literature, they knew that samples of homosexuals who had been studied were, for the most part, clinic patients, and that our knowledge of homosexuality is therefore fragmentary. The opportunity to talk with a trained professional person who had a genuine interest in them as individuals and in every aspect of their life patterns was, as some frequently reported, a rewarding experience, especially because of my completely accepting and morally nonjudgmental attitude toward homosexual behavior. Over the course of the years, many of them have come to see me not only as a friend rather than a detached scientist—and correctly so—but also as a person with knowledge of psychiatric, legal, and other expert resources in the community from which assistance in times of trouble can be obtained. It will be apparent that the motivations are much more complex than indicated in these brief statements.

When the research was begun in 1954, the primary objectives were to study the developmental sequences in the life history of the individual leading to adult identification as a male homosexual and to determine the correlates in personality structure and adjustment of such an identification. It very quickly became apparent that in order to understand the adjustment patterns of such individuals, it would be necessary to study the sectors of the homosexual subculture in which many of them participated. A study of homosexual subcultures soon became a project in its own right. As I have described in greater detail in previous reports the procedures and difficulties involved in this ethnographic or field study method (1961, 1963), I shall repeat here only the fact that my effort is to look with the subject at his life and his world through his eyes as he sees it; to be as fully an "insider" or participant as one who is "wise" but not a member can be. Looking with him at his world is a multiphasic process, involving going with him to scenes, occasions, or social settings in which the activities are occurring that constitute some of the essential features of his homosexual world, and interviewing him about those activities before and after such occasions. Thus I have participated with most of the thirty subjects, and many additional ones, in a wide variety of social activities in their homes and/or other social settings, as well as interviewing and testing them in my home study.

Because of the long-sustained character of the inquiry, the repeated checks on life history data at intervals, the participation with the research subjects in other social activities, and the positive relationship with them, I have a high degree of confidence that the data are to be trusted.

In my initial interviews, which were relatively unstructured and tape recorded, I formulated the task as a joint enterprise between the subject and myself, in which the objective was to understand as much about his life history, including the present, as possible. A general statement was made to the effect that this would include, among other things, his relations with his parents, siblings, and friends; his educational career; occupational career; sexual history; health history; fantasies; and his hopes, worries, and satisfactions. Sometimes I was asked whether I was doing another Kinsey study, to which I always replied that I was not, and that although I wanted to learn about their sexual histories and current sexual activities, I was at least equally interested, if not more so, in other aspects of their lives. Unless information about sexual experience was given spontaneously in the course of relating other information, direct questions were not asked until a given period in the life history had been completed, such as childhood to age twelve, or adolescence to age eighteen.

The initial interviews varied from two to four sessions of two or three hours' duration. Five years later, all thirty subjects were re-interviewed, in order to fill gaps in the data, to follow the changes occurring in their lives, and to check on the reliability of the first interview. At this time, the entire sexual history was reviewed with the subject. In the third series of interviews, three years later, one area of intensive probing was the sexual, with a series of questions that focused on the total cycle of experience and behavior from the beginning of a given dyadic sexual sequence to its completion. If, for example, a subject reported that he went out to look for a sexual partner, I asked him to describe in detail what happened from the time he met the sexual partner until they separated, including every detail, if possible, of the sexual activity. This step-by-step procedure not only produced new information about feelings, fantasies, sexual practices, and problems, but also made it difficult for the subject to reply with evasive generalities.

These interviews produced extreme discomfort in many subjects. Often expressed at the end of the interview was the statement, "It's a good thing you didn't ask these questions in the first interview." The questions, "What is your preferred method of achieving sexual gratification?" or "What kind of sexual activities do you and your partner engage in?" or "Do you prefer fellatio or anal intercourse?" were answered without apparent discomfort. The question—if a preferred method is fellatio—"*How* do you perform fellatio?" is a much more disturbing one. One subject who had described sexual patterns without noticeable anxiety or evasion could not respond to this request, and said, "In all the years and the many hours in which I have talked with you, this is the first time I have been ashamed. I simply cannot do it." I did not press it.[4]

SEXUAL PATTERNS

The range of erotic sensitivity, the preferred or accepted mode and conditions for achieving sexual gratification, the nature of sexual gratification, and the frequency with which

---

[4] The cooperation of these subjects, and their willingness to allow me to probe the most private aspects of their experience in great detail during extended hours of interview, were remarkable, in view of the fact that they were not clinical patients. Their disturbance, when asked about the details of *how* they performed particular sexual acts, is puzzling. I am indebted to Dr. Harold Garfinkel for the suggestion that it may be due to the fact that I asked them to make sexuality a *technically* describable project. I did not press this particular subject because I already had extensive material from him concerning his sexual behavior and erotic fantasies. In this necessarily brief paper, it is not possible to document the detail and depth of the interview material. In the full published report, this documentation will be provided.

it is sought, vary from one individual to another.[5] Some general patterns may, however, be distinguished. The major modes of achieving sexual gratification are fellatio, anal intercourse, masturbation, and body friction—or any combination thereof.

In my sample of thirty, 43 percent (thirteen) prefer and predominantly practice fellatio. Two of these men prefer and predominantly perform fellatio on the partner, but on occasion accept anal insertion by the partner. One man prefers and predominantly performs reciprocal or mutual fellatio, but also occasionally engages in anal intercourse, without preference for position or role. Ten men will not now practice any form of anal activity, although all have done so, with varying frequencies, in the past. They now reject such practices for a variety of reasons—including fear of venereal disease, lack of sexual and/or emotional pleasure, experience of pain, or feelings of revulsion. Eight of the ten prefer and predominantly practice reciprocal or mutual fellatio with the partner; and the other two prefer to perform fellatio on the partner. The nine individuals who prefer mutual or reciprocal fellatio also engage in mutual masturbation, either as fore-pleasure or as an alternate form of achieving orgasm. Bieber and his co-authors (1962) use the term "insertee" to describe the sex roles of accepting the penis of the partner in either the oral or anal orifice, and the term "insertor" for the role of inserting the penis in either orifice of the partner. Using this terminology, four of the thirteen men who prefer fellatio are predominantly oral insertees; and nine assume both the insertee and insertor roles, simultaneously as in mutual fellatio ("69"), or in succession.

Seven of the thirty (23 percent) express no preference for any particular form of sexual activity, and engage in and enjoy all of the major forms of homosexual practices. An additional seven (23 percent) express preferences, but engage in and enjoy all forms, accommodating to the situation—which includes the wishes of the partner, the emotional response to

[5] Data on the frequency with which sexual experience is sought and/or obtained are not presented in this paper, but will be included in the full published report, as will a discussion of the data on variations in the meaning and nature of sexual gratification.

the partner, and the duration of the relationship with the partner. Preferences may shift with a change of partner, so that, for example, if the partner is perceived as "more masculine," the preference may be to assume the insertee role. If, on the other hand, the partner is perceived as "less masculine," the preference may be to assume the insertor role. (This example should not be generalized to all subjects.) Thus, fourteen of the thirty (46 percent) either have no preference or adjust their preference to the situation, so that the terms, predominantly insertee or predominantly insertor, cannot be used to characterize them.

Only two of the thirty (6 percent) prefer and predominantly assume the insertor role in both anal and oral sexual activity. Both have living relationships with partners who prefer the insertee role. Very rarely, these two men assume the insertee role, usually with other partners.

Finally, one man in the group prefers mutual masturbation, and will engage in mutual fellatio on occasion, but rejects any form of anal practice.

In summary, then: (1) for only six (20 percent) of the sample can the sexual preference and predominant practice be characterized as fitting into an insertee or insertor sex role (four are oral insertees, and two are insertors with no preference for anal or oral orifices); (2) nine (30 percent) of the group, who prefer and predominantly practice fellatio, assume both the insertee and the insertor roles, simultaneously or in succession with the same partner; (3) fourteen (46 percent) either express no preference and engage in all of the major forms of homosexual activity or, in spite of expressed preferences, adjust and accommodate to the situation, so that, depending on the partner, both the insertee and insertor roles are assumed, and no predominant role can be assigned. Perhaps the most striking finding is the fact that so few individuals prefer and predominantly engage in modes of sexual gratification for which any term defining a typical "sex role" can be assigned. Variability, interchangeability, and interpartner accommodation seem to preclude role categorizations for the majority.

Other studies of sexual practices and preferences of

male homosexuals corroborate the fact that a sizable proportion of them express no preference and engage in all forms of
homosexual activity, or, despite expressed preferences, perform
a wide variety of sexual acts. Bieber and his co-authors (1962)
reported this finding in their study of 106 homosexual patients.
Their sample included bisexuals as well as exclusive homosexuals. Roughly a quarter of their group expressed no preference and could not be assigned to the categories of being predominantly insertors or insertees. Of their group, 36 percent
were predominantly insertors and 31 percent were predominantly insertees. This is a much larger percentage of individuals who can be classified in one or the other of these two
categories than in my sample. The percentage figures of those
who express no preference and engage in all forms of homosexual activity are, however, comparable (23 percent in my
group and 24 percent in the Bieber sample). An analysis of
my 1954 data shows a higher percentage of those who were
predominantly insertees or insertors. At that time, 23 percent
would have been classified as insertees, and 17 percent as
insertors—a total of 40 percent, as contrasted with 20 percent
in 1962. It cannot be too strongly emphasized that sexual
preferences and practices of many homosexuals change over
time as a function of many variables, including participation
in homosexual subcultures, relationships with living partners,
and age. Part of the discrepancy between the findings of the
Bieber study and my own may possibly be accounted for by
my long-term follow-up methods.

Westwood's study (1960) of 127 individuals, who were
predominantly homosexual, also corroborates the finding that
a sizable proportion of these individuals cannot be readily
assigned a preference in sexual role, although his figures are
given in such form that it is difficult to derive an exact percentage.

Finally, data obtained from the Venereal Disease Clinic
of the Los Angeles City Health Department and reported by
the writer in 1962 show the same trend. Two hundred and fifty-
three males treated for venereal disease in the City Health
Clinic and interviewed for sexual contacts who might have
become similarly infected named only other males. When asked

to describe their sexual preferences and patterns, a majority, 54.5 percent, whose sexual preference was for anal intercourse, expressed no preference for the "dominant" or the "receptive role" (terms used by City Health personnel, which are interchangeable with the terms "insertor" and "insertee" as used by Bieber and his co-authors [1962]). Only 27 percent prefer and restrict their practices to the receptive role and 18.2 percent, to the dominant role in anal intercourse. It is of some interest that only 5 percent of this sample admitted to the practice of fellatio, a figure in strong contrast with those obtained in other samples already described. This finding may be a function of the stressful character of the interview situation.

In this discussion of preferences and predominant sexual practices, I have deliberately avoided the terms *active* and *passive*. Commenting on the fact that *activity* and *passivity* are psychological concepts and that to relate them to sexual activities is misleading, Bieber and his co-authors (1962) (as already noted) have substituted the terms *insertor* and *insertee*. "In the act of fellatio, for example," they write (pp. 238–239), "it is incorrect to judge one participant as 'active' and the other 'passive.' Is the individual who is using his mouth as receptor in the act of sucking, passive? From a kinetic orientation he is not. It becomes clear that concepts of activity and passivity to describe role behavior are not operationally useful."

I agree that the terms *active* and *passive* to describe sex roles of homosexuals should be discarded because they are inaccurate and misleading. Also, their continued use perpetuates a stereotyped dichotomy not only of sexual preferences or roles but of associated psychological attitudes as well. The individual who assumes the insertee role, either orally or anally, may not only be the initiator of the activity and the more active one from a kinetic standpoint but may also control it in the most actively aggressive way. The insertor, on the other hand, may submit to action performed on him with relatively little activity, from a kinetic standpoint, or control of the action. Even in those instances in which the individual assumes one or the other sex role exclusively or predominantly, the way in which he performs the role can vary so greatly that the one constant is whether the penis of one is or is not in an oral or anal orifice of the other. Who is active or passive, controlled or controlling, possessor or possessed cannot be determined merely by designating the act performed. The terms *active* and *passive* may be as inaccurate in describing sex roles and correlated psychological attitudes in heterosexual dyads as in homosexual ones. Although the terms *passivity* and *activity* may be useful in referring to psychological states, their correlation with gender and sex roles is at least questionable, in the light of cross-cultural evidence; for example, Ford and Beach (1951) and Mead (1961).

GENDER IDENTITY AND SEXUAL PATTERNS

Let us consider now some problems of gender identity, as found in my highly selected sample of male homosexuals. That they are not representative of all homosexuals, nor that all "types" are represented, has already been indicated and will become even more clear in the discussion which follows. I shall use the term *male gender identity* to refer to *all* that distinguishes males from females: including patterns of skills, occupation, dress and adornment, gestures, demeanor, emotional expression, erotic fantasies, and sexual behavior. Many of these patterns show such wide cultural variation that it is generally assumed that a large portion of psychological masculinity or femininity, or of the psychological attributes of gender identity, are culturally determined. To behave as a man or to assume the masculine gender role in one cultural setting may thus, as Mead (1961) and others have shown, require attitudes and behavior that are almost the polar opposite of those in another cultural setting. The problem of determining the basic psychological attributes of masculinity and femininity that cut across all cultural variations is one for which there are few answers on which behavioral or social scientists would agree.

In our society, irrespective of the degree to which the male homosexual fulfils the male gender role expectations in all other respects, he fails, according to societal judgment, in at least one: he is inappropriately erotically focused on males, not females. It is probably true that gender identity problems result in the failure to fulfil male gender role expectations, and that additional ones are created by the failure. How he resolves these problems, or whether he resolves them, is therefore a matter of considerable interest.

The working solution,[6] as the subject perceives it, is, of course, only part of the story, because, as is self-evident, there are many components of gender identity of which the subject is unaware. In this paper, however, we shall look primarily at the solutions from the subjective standpoint of the individual, recognizing that it is an incomplete account. From that standpoint there are, it seems to me, three major types of working solutions to the problem of masculine gender identity in these subjects.[7] All of these men perceive themselves appropriately as biological males, and all now consciously prefer to be males. It should be made clear that none would surrender his biological maleness. For this group, however, the problem of psychological gender (that is, masculinity–femininity) is a complex one.

The first solution is to accept the masculine–feminine psychological gender dichotomy *for homosexuality* and place oneself at one or other of these poles. The man who accepts this dichotomy and places himself at the masculine pole usually chooses between two alternatives. He may define himself as a *masculine* homosexual and point to occupation or athletic interests, emotional ease, or satisfaction and success in occupational and social associations with nonhomosexual males, to show that he is masculine. In sexual practice he predominantly engages in anal intercourse in the insertor position or accepts fellation, and he points to this fact as additional evidence that he is a masculine homosexual. Only two individuals in my

---

[6] The term *solution* may convey more to the reader than I intend, and may be ill-chosen. Although some coming to terms with problems is implied, no inferences should be made about the degree to which a particular "solution" represents a full resolution of the problem.

[7] All the subjects have been given a battery of psychological tests, which includes the TAT, Rorschach, and Sentence Completion, as well as standard psychological inventories with M–F subscales, and other measures of psychological femininity–masculinity. Erotic fantasies and some dream material have been obtained in interviews. All these materials provide rich sources of data for the other components of gender identity in these subjects. A detailed account of the intensive interview procedures used in eliciting the data from which the three types of solution have been formulated cannot be given in this brief paper.

sample adopt this solution. As indicated in the discussion of sexual patterns, both have living relationships with partners who prefer the insertee role. Both have occupations that would be rated as masculine. In manner, demeanor, gesture, and speech they present a masculine appearance. Neither of them has pronounced esthetic interests; one, in fact, is preoccupied almost exclusively, outside his occupation, with participant or spectator sports. I should make it clear that although they take pride in their masculinity, there does not appear to be any defensive exaggeration of the fact. (It may be pointed out parenthetically that there are sectors of the homosexual sub-culture in which masculinity is caricatured in the affectation of symbols of masculine toughness, as, for example, in the "motor-cycle" or "leather" set.) One man appears to accept and enjoy his homosexuality without anxiety and guilt and has no wish, or sees no reason why he should want, to change his pattern. The other is consciously remorseful and guilty about his homo-sexuality, although he does not believe that it would be pos-sible for him to change and has made no conscious effort to do so.

The other alternative for the man who accepts the mas-culine–feminine dichotomy for homosexuals and places himself at the masculine pole, is to separate the sexual and nonsexual aspects of the masculine role; and while pointing to "male" qualities such as aggressiveness, domination, decision-making, and control of emotionality, to assert that he is the masculine partner in any homosexual relationship, despite the fact that he engages in a variety of sexual practices. His occupation would be rated as highly masculine, and he occupies a posi-tion of considerable authority, involving the supervision of many men. Like the first two already described, his general bearing, speech, and manner are not effeminate in any way. He combines, to an unusual degree, leisure-time pursuits indi-cating high esthetic interest and talent, and ones requiring what would ordinarily be considered to be masculine skills. It is unfortunate that I cannot specify his interests in greater detail, but to do so would be to run the risk of identifying him. His preference and predominant sexual practice is mutual fellatio, and he does not and will not engage in anal activity, for medical and esthetic reasons. Although he sees himself as a masculine homosexual, he is quite conscious of his own culturally defined femininity, in terms of his esthetic interests, and does not appear to exaggerate his masculinity in any defensive way. His feelings about being homosexual are in conflict and are ambivalent.

For the man who accepts the masculine–feminine dichotomy and places himself in the feminine half, the most extreme position closely approaches transvestism; and perhaps the most vivid description is that given by Rechy (1963) of "Miss Destiny." He may insist on the insertee role in anal intercourse or fellatio, and in manner, occupation, and interest display his femininity. None of these individuals is in my sample. Nine individuals in the sample, however, describe themselves as feminine homosexuals, and display this femininity in varying degrees. Although they see themselves as clearly and unmistakably male, they do not see themselves as masculine; and most of them express the wish to be more masculine. All of them are now in occupations in which there are probably as many women as men, and these occupations do not carry a distinctive gender connotation. In general, it is characteristic of this group that they feel uncomfortable in the presence of markedly heterosexual men, especially in social situations, and very often in work situations. With one exception, they have pronounced esthetic and/or feminine interests. With the same exception, all of them have gone through a period of dressing in women's clothing, either in private or on social occasions involving other homosexuals. Some of them continue to do so on such occasions. In careful questioning about conscious fantasies and motivations experienced during such cross-dressing, all of them make it clear that they were *pretending* to be women but that they did not have conscious wishes to be women or biological females. It is essential, however, that the question of unconscious motivations or fantasies in such behavior remain open for examination. When, for example, an individual goes to a Halloween party dressed as a pregnant woman, even though he does not make strenuous efforts to conceal the fact that he is a man-dressed-as-a-pregnant-woman, the motivational problems become very complex. It is also

important to note at this point that attitudes toward femininity
and display of femininity in homosexual societies are very
much influenced by social factors operating in the group as
well as in the individual motivations of the members. The
sexual patterns of these nine individuals are predominantly
oral. Four of them are predominantly oral insertees, and five
assume both the insertee and insertor roles in reciprocal or
mutual fellatio.

One man in this group is of especial interest because
he illustrates in his developmental history the most extreme
feminization of the entire group and also illustrates the influence of participation in homosexual groups on changes in
sexual patterns, as well as on conscious fantasies and other expressions of psychological femininity in a homosexual male.
In his early adolescence—about the age of thirteen—he began
to dress in women's clothing, both when alone with a young
boy friend and in the presence of the relatives with whom he
was living. With what he reports to be the complete cooperation of his aunt, he acquired a fairly extensive feminine ward-
robe, and was complimented on how much he resembled a
girl both by the aunt and by his schoolmates when, on some
occasions of costume parties, he dressed as a girl. He reports
that he was "pretending to be a girl," and that at times he
longed "to be a girl" because he "liked to have the kind of
attention men would give to a girl when they were paying
court to her." One of his favorite fantasies was that of being
Madame Pompadour. He would admire himself in the mirror
and have fantasies of men coming to admire him. He makes it
clear, however, that he did not fantasy himself as being a
biological female; that is, as having breasts and a vagina, and
no penis. When questioned about whether he had ever wanted
to have his body changed from that of male to a female, he
was very firm in his negative answer. From the age of thirteen,
when this cross-dressing began, until about the age of twenty,
when he found and entered a homosexual group in the university which he attended, he experienced very conflicting
feelings and considerable guilt about this behavior. Very early
in his active homosexual life—which began when he was about
eighteen years of age—his preference and predominant prac-

tice in sexual activity was to assume the insertee role in anal intercourse. During the act he would have a "fantasy of himself as a woman." When questioned about what this meant, he replied that he was in the "passive role and the partner was using an opening, as they would with a woman." He sought homosexual partners whom he perceived to be "masculine." When I first interviewed him, he had been living with his present living-partner for several years, and his fantasies and sexual pattern were beginning to change. His partner strongly disapproved of effeminacy and cross-dressing and exerted influence on him to become more masculine. Partly to accommodate the partner, the sexual pattern between them began to change to mutual or reciprocal fellatio, and on occasion he would assume the insertor role in anal intercourse. In the last interview (he is now in his early forties), he reports that he no longer cross-dresses nor has any conscious fantasies of being a woman, but wishes to be more "aggressive" and "manly." He sometimes has fantasies of being "dominated by other men or taken by force by other men," but thinks of himself as a man in that situation. The progressive change in him is evidenced not only in his report but also in his general appearance, demeanor, and greatly increased self-assurance. It is significant that he believes that the change had to do with the people he associated with in homosexual groups and that if he had been in a group which approved of effeminate behavior and crossdressing he would have continued with his early patterns. One final remark about this individual is that he is on the borderline of adopting the solution that will be described next.

The second major working solution to the gender identity problems is that adopted by those who do not accept the masculine–feminine dichotomy for themselves and reject it as undesirable in others. They then define themselves as male *and* homosexual: they reject sexual performance and erotic object choice as the critical criterion of maleness and masculinity; they accept the concept of the masculine–feminine *continuum* (not dichotomy) on the basis of psychological attributes; and they place themselves somewhere toward the masculine end of this continuum. Seventeen of the sample are in this category. (A description of one pair of men who are in this group, and who have established a living relationship of some duration, is given in a later section of this paper.) The majority are individuals who, as previously described, either have no preference for particular forms of sexual activity and engage in and enjoy most forms, or, in spite of preference, accommodate to the situation. The stability of this solution varies greatly. For some, there is a constant struggle to maintain the position. One man, for example, who in the early interviews equated homosexuality with "not being a man, and being feminine," no longer makes this equation—but the struggle to maintain a self-image as masculine and homosexual continues. Some others in the group seem not to have had any struggle in reaching this solution or maintaining it. For some of these, this may be accounted for in part by the fact that they have masculine occupations, and in appearance, manner, and interests show no evidence of conspicuous femininity. For some individuals who have achieved this solution, the primary problems cannot be described as gender problems but as problems involving control, domination, power, aggression, and initiative with their love and/or sexual partners. They may have once defined the wish to be possessed or to be dominated or to be controlled as feminine. Many of these are now able to see these motivations in their own right, apart from their imputed gender connotations.

The third working solution is the one which has been characterized as the "third sex" or "intermediate sex." This is the position expressed by only one person in the sample, who perceives himself, and thinks of other male homosexuals, as being both male and female, psychologically. In his manner, gestures, and speech there is nothing which could be described as effeminate. He is a professional man, in an occupational field which is preponderantly entered by men. He has high esthetic interests and talents. He is one of those who express no preference for any particular mode of sexual activity and engage in all forms, with equal pleasure.

From the data presented in the preceding discussion, it is clear that for the majority of the individuals in this particular sample there is no apparent correspondence between a conscious sense of gender identity and a preferred or predominant role in sexual activity. For the four individuals who are predominantly oral insertees in sexual practice and who accept the masculine–feminine dichotomy for homosexuality, their perception of themselves as being in the feminine half of that dichotomy shows a congruence between psychological gender and sex role. The two individuals who are predominantly insertors and who perceive themselves as masculine homosexuals also show the presumed congruence. For the remainder, however, as we have seen, the sexual pattern cannot be categorized in terms of a predominant role, and the consciousness of masculinity or femininity appears to bear no clear relation to particular sexual patterns.

HOMOSEXUAL SUBCULTURE EFFECTS

For an interpretation of these findings, it may be helpful to remind ourselves that all of these men were obtained from homosexual groups and friendship networks; that they are committed to a homosexual way of life; and that their personal and social identities as homosexuals have been defined, in part, over the course of continuous social interaction with other homosexuals. Their entry into an active homosexual life may occur in a large variety of ways, and the particular group, setting, or sector of that life which they enter, or into which they subsequently move, may vary enormously. There are many homosexual worlds or subcultures, loosely linked by friendship and acquaintance networks, but differing greatly in normative expectations, which may in part determine the degree of gender and sex role differentiation, the criteria for and indices of masculinity, the expectation of effeminate behavior in gesture, speech, dress, and gait, the criteria for selection of appropriate sex or love partners, and the modes of sexual gratification.

The world of the hustler, as described by Rechy (1963) (also by Reiss [1961] and Ross [1959], with some variations), in which sex roles for the hustler and his "score" are rigidly defined, in which the appearance of "tough masculinity" must be cultivated assiduously by the hustler, and sexual gratification for the hustler is understood to be a by-product in a monetary transaction, is completely foreign to and rejected by most of the men whom I have interviewed. In strongest contrast is the world of a group of men organized for social purposes, most of whom are college graduates and members of a fraternity. Informal standards of selection maintain a loose membership of individuals who take pride in the fact that they are masculine in appearance and manner and indistinguishable from their business and professional heterosexual associates. Effeminacy in gesture, dress, or speech excludes a prospective applicant, or provides grounds for quiet expulsion if it occurs in a member. Love and/or sex partners must meet the same standards in appearance and behavior, and a social introduction (in contrast to anonymous casual pickups) is a necessary prelude to an affair. Sex role differentiation between partners is unusual, and gender connotations of sexual practice are minimized or tend to disappear because both partners engage in most or all of the major forms of homosexual practice. In other informal social groups composed of one or more clique and/or friendship or acquaintance networks, sex role differentiation, with clear-cut gender connotations that are generalized to nonsexual aspects of the relations between temporary or more permanent partners, may be usual. There is some reason to believe that this is more common in lower socioeconomic groups, and, if so, would correspond to the clearer differentiation in the heterosexual world at that class level—but the evidence is too slight to be more than speculative.

Between these rather sharp extremes, social groups form in which there are few, if any, normative expectations and in which all degrees of gender and sex role differentiation occur. In some of these groups, the concern with masculinity–femininity is reflected in frequent discussions of who is "the husband" and who is "the wife" in a given pair, the assumption being that there is some differential in masculinity between the two and/or a corresponding difference in preferred sex role. Very often, even among intimate friends, the fact that the sexual practices do not correspond to the presumed differences in masculinity–femininity between members of the pair is a closely guarded secret. In other groups, while comparisons of masculinity–femininity may be frequently made, the assignment of gender role in any terminology borrowed from the two-sexed heterosexual world is derogated, and every effort is made to resist comparisons with heterosexual marriage and its differential gender and sex role prescriptions.

Homosexual bars also play a large part in the social life of many homosexuals, both for those who have an active social life in groups outside and for others who have few such associations. The bars vary greatly in the clientele that they attract and the informal rules or standards that they promote concerning effeminate display. In some bars, for example, obvious effeminacy in dress or demeanor is not only frowned upon but may be a sufficient reason for the refusal of admission. In other bars, there are no standards of admission, and the most obvious display of effeminacy may be found, so that the clues to biological maleness and femaleness are blurred and judgments are uncertain.

Individuals may move from one sector of the homosexual world to another at different stages in their homosexual careers, so that rather striking changes in behavior patterns and accompanying psychological gender identity may occur. For example, some of the men in my sample who are now in their forties, and who are masculine appearing in their general demeanor and deplore obvious display of femininity, report that when they first entered into an active homosexual life they were highly effeminate and frequently dressed in elaborate feminine costumes for ceremonial occasions in the homosexual world.

The many homosexual worlds or subcultures in which a homosexual may spend a large part of his social, leisure, or recreational life outside his work are only briefly sketched in the foregoing account. They form a very loose aggregate of deviant collectivities. An individual may move back and forth, from one to another, with or without full participation in any one.

This account is intended to draw attention to the importance of homosexual milieux or subcultures in helping to determine attitudes toward homosexuality, consciousness of and manifestations of masculinity and femininity, and the connotations attached to particular sex roles. It is clear that subculture effects constitute only one set of variables, which interact with many other variables, such as personality dynamics and structure, personal appearance (including body build, gesture, demeanor), age, and occupation, to produce these attitudes, self-concepts, and behavior. Most accounts of gender identity and sex roles in male homosexuals focus on personality traits and psychodynamics and ignore the important contribution of the shared perspectives of homosexual subcultures.

INDIVIDUAL PAIRS

Although reference has been made in the foregoing account to differences in homosexual pairs with respect to differentiation of sex and gender role in relation to the subculture context, it should be noted that individual pairs work out individual solutions, although influenced by that context.

It has often been said that the homosexual is unable to sustain continuous relationships for any period of time. To quote Bieber and his co-authors (1962, p. 317):

> Some homosexuals tend to seek out a single relationship, hoping to gratify all emotional needs within a one-to-one exclusive relationship. Such twosomes are usually based on unrealistic expectations, often accompanied by inordinate demands; in most instances, these pairs are caught up in a turbulent, abrasive attachment. These liaisons are characterized by initial excitement which may include exaltation and confidence in the discovery of a great love which soon alternates with anxiety, rage, and depression as magical expectations are inevitably frustrated. Gratification of magical wishes is symbolically sought in homosexual activity which is intense in the early phase of a new "affair." These relationships are generally disrupted after a period of several months to a year or so; they are generally sought anew with another partner and the cycle starts again.

Although this is an accurate characterization of many homosexual liaisons, it does not apply to a number of pairs whom I have interviewed.

First some data from my sample on the duration of relationships. Of the thirty subjects, eight are at present in living relationships that they have sustained for periods of from nine to fifteen years. One of these has sustained a monogamous relationship for ten years. Five have sustained sexual relationships with the partner, although they are not monogamous. One maintained a monogamous relationship for four years; and although he still has occasional sexual experience with his living-partner, most of his sexual relations during the past eleven years have occurred outside. One man in this group sustained a sexual relationship with his partner for eleven years, with occasional outside contacts, but for the last three years sexual experience with his partner has ceased.

An additional eight individuals in the sample have sustained relationships, either in the past or at the present time, for from five to eight years. In one of these relationships, which lasted five years, there was continuous monogamy. In the other seven, the sexuality between the members of each pair continued, but they also engaged in sexual contacts outside the relationship. Four of the thirty subjects have had a series of living relationships lasting from two to four years. For one individual only, monogamy was sustained in each relationship. None of the remaining ten individuals has sustained a living-relationship that was sexual in character for more than a few months.

All but three of the thirty individuals are seekers of dyadic relationships. They express an intense longing for relationships with stability, sexual continuity, intimacy, love, and affection. It is beyond the scope of this paper to analyze the complex personality and social variables that prevent so many from achieving their expressed objective.

Now to turn to two illustrative pairs.

The two men in the first pair have lived together for ten years and have maintained a monogamous relationship. Both define themselves as male *and* homosexual. One is in his middle thirties and the other in his early forties. Both are college graduates and successful professional men. They are achievement-oriented and continue to pursue advanced study in their respective professional fields. They own their own home, in a suburban area. I have visited them in their home on a number of social occasions. The house has been transformed by them from a mediocre dwelling to a home, and a home that is both comfortable and esthetically attractive. One member of the pair is more dogmatic, methodical, literal-minded, and high in mechanical aptitude and interests. The other is more emotionally responsive and expansive, and his interests are directed toward humanistic studies and the arts. In the emotional problems that arise from these differences, whether over a major or minor issue, it is the second man who appears to be the guardian of the emotional life of the relationship and who has the temperament and the capacity to work through the problems. Although they are devoted to each other and to the continuation of the relationship, one assumes more of the "expressive" functions and the other the "instrumental" functions. Such role differentiation is very common in those homosexual pairs which are able successfully to achieve a sustained and valued relationship.

They are perceived by some of their friends as differing in masculinity and femininity, and they perceive themselves in this way. The difference is not apparent to me. However, the one who perceives himself as somewhat less masculine than his partner is the one who has been described as carrying more of the expressive functions in the relationship. Over the course of the years, areas of shared interests have developed, especially in music, the theatre, and travel.

The task roles they assume in the management of the household are jointly distributed on the basis of preferences, talents, and accommodation to work schedules. The one who has been described as having a higher mechanical aptitude performs the tasks of household repair; he also does the cooking, for which he has a superb talent. The other household tasks, such as housecleaning and shopping, are largely performed by the other member of the pair. There is nothing rigid about this distribution of responsibilities.

Their sexual relationship, which is described by them as being increasingly pleasurable and gratifying, does not fit into any sex role dichotomy. They engage in all of the major forms of homosexual practice. They alternate and vary the sex roles assumed. Mutual sexual pleasure and gratification are important for both. It is not possible to ascribe a more dominant, masculine, controlling sex role, or a more passive, feminine, submissive sex role, to one or the other. At the beginning of their relationship, such differences apparently did exist; but over the course of their years together, these have disappeared.

Neither of these men participates in the "gay round of life." In part, this is due to their occupational placement: they cannot afford to run the risk of becoming publicly known as homosexuals. They are determined that they will not live in a "half world." They make a very conscious effort to cultivate heterosexual friends. Their social life also involves relations with homosexual couples like themselves. On occasion, they attend small homosexual parties of friends.

The second pair of men are now in their early fifties and have lived together for fifteen years. Neither completed the first year of high school. Both are clerks, one in an industrial firm and the other in a retail store. The sexual relationship between them was maintained for the first four years. They then began to seek sexual relationships outside, and the sexuality between them gradually ceased. They live together in a home, not simply as roommates—a term that is very often used in the homosexual world—but as a "married" pair. Both men are somewhat feminine in gesture and general demeanor and probably could be identified as homosexuals by anyone who was "wise." Both think of themselves as having been born as homosexuals. There is no evidence in their histories that they have struggled against it or thought of it as anything other than their "natural way of life." Although sexual attraction between them has completely disappeared, affection, devotion, and a feeling of joint responsibility for each other continue—and it looks very much as though it will end only at death. Their predominant sexual practices with each other at the beginning, and now with others outside, are oral; and both of them now primarily assume the insertee role with their sexual partners.

The masculine–feminine differential in this pair is simply a matter of household jokes, because both recognize that there is very little difference between them in this respect. While they divide the responsibilities and tasks involved in maintaining the household, there appears to be no gender differentiation in this distribution. As in the first pair, however, one man appears to assume more responsibility, and is more effective, in managing the emotional tensions that arise between them. In contrast to the first pair, they are very active in the "gay life." They go to many homosexual parties and to gay bars, chiefly in the neighborhood in which they live. In the homosexual social circles in which they move, the "husband–wife" dichotomy is usually clear-cut, and sexual relationships outside the pair are accepted as commonplace. At the beginning of their relationship, the male–female dichotomy in nonsexual spheres was emphasized. Gradually the differentiation has disappeared.

My purpose in selecting these two pairs is simply to illustrate two ways in which male homosexuals may sustain a living-relationship over a long period of time in a manner that appears to be mutually gratifying. They are not intended as necessarily typical of those individuals in my sample who have sustained living relationships over a long period of time. There are some pairs whose relationship must be characterized as an abrasive attachment, with tormenting periods of jealousy and rage, and with frequent threats to separate. One such pair in my sample has sustained this stormy relationship for fifteen years, and will probably continue to do so.

Living relationships of such long duration in the homosexual world are probably unusual, although there is some reason to believe that they may be more common than the clinician is led to believe by his sample of those who seek help. In selecting such pairs for purposes of illustration, I do not want to distort the picture. As will have been apparent from the data on duration of relationships in my sample, for many homosexuals one-night-stands or short-term relationships are typical.

CONCLUDING COMMENT

I have proposed in this paper that our concepts of sex roles and their relationship to psychological gender identity in male homosexuals who are committed to a homosexual way of life require revision. I have also proposed that an expanded theoretical framework that will include variations in homosexual subcultures and social interaction between members of pairs may be useful.

The data which have given rise to these proposals have indicated that for the majority of the individuals in my particular sample there is no apparent correspondence between a conscious sense of gender identity and a preferred or predominant role in sexual activity. Except for a small minority, the sexual pattern cannot be categorized in terms of a predominant role, and the consciousness of masculinity or femininity appears to bear no clear relation to particular sexual patterns. Comparisons of homosexual subcultures indicate that the degree to which sex roles and gender roles are clearly differentiated varies greatly with the subculture. Cultural variables, as well as personality variables, appear to be important in defining prescribed or acceptable masculinity or femininity and/or sex roles. The relations between individual pairs appear to be additional determinants of the variations in sexual patterns and gender identity.

SUMMARY

Data are presented on sexual patterns and psychological gender identities of thirty predominantly or exclusively homosexual males who have been intensively interviewed at intervals over a period of eight years. The research subjects were obtained from homosexual cliques and friendship networks; they were committed to homosexuality and were not seeking therapeutic assistance.

The sexual patterns of a majority of these subjects cannot be categorized into clearly differentiated sex roles because of the variability and interchangeability of practices with the same partner or different partners. Psychological gender identity as perceived by these subjects appears to bear little relation to sexual practice. A variety of working solutions to the problem of psychological gender identity in homosexual males is discussed.

Comparisons of homosexual subcultures indicate that the degree to which sex roles and gender roles are clearly differentiated varies greatly with the subculture. The relations between individual pairs—especially those who sustain a living relationship of some duration—appear to be additional determinants of the variations in sexual patterns and gender identity.

It is proposed that concepts of sex roles and their relations to psychological gender identities in male homosexuals require revision, and that an expanded theoretical framework which will include variations in homosexual subcultures and social interaction between members of pairs may be useful.

REFERENCES

BIEBER, I., DAIN, H. J., DINCE, P. R., DRELLICH, M. G., GRAND, H. G., GUNDLACH, R. H., KREMER, M. W., RIFKIN, A. H., WILBUR, C. B., AND BIEBER, T. B. 1962 *Homosexuality.* New York: Basic Books, Inc.

BROWN, D. G. 1958 Inversion and homosexuality. *Amer. J. Orthopsychiat. 28,* 424–429.

BROWN, D. G. 1961 Transvestism and sex-role inversion. In A. Ellis, and A. Abarbanel (Eds.), *The encyclopedia of sexual behavior,* Vol. II. New York: Hawthorn Books, Inc.

FERENCZI, S. 1914 The nosology of male homosexuality (homoerotism). (Translated by Ernest Jones.) In *Sex in psychoanalysis* (1950). New York: Basic Books, Inc.

FORD, C. S., AND BEACH, F. A. 1951 *Patterns of sexual behavior.* New York: Harper and Row.

HOOKER, E. 1957 The adjustment of the male overt homosexual. *J. proj. Tech. 21,* 18–31.

HOOKER, E. 1958 Male homosexuality in the Rorschach. *J. proj. Tech. 22,* 33–54.

HOOKER, E. 1961 The homosexual community. Paper read at the XIV International Congress of Applied Psychology. Published 1962 in *Personality research* (Vol. 2 of *Proceedings of the XIV International Congress of Applied Psychology*). Copenhagen: Munksgaard Press.

HOOKER, E. 1962 Life styles of male homosexuals and venereal disease. Paper read at World Forum on Syphilis and Other Treponematoses. In press, U. S. Public Health Reports.

HOOKER, E. 1963 Male homosexuality. In N. L. Farberow (Ed.), *Taboo topics.* New York: Atherton Press.

MEAD, M. 1961 Cultural determinants of sexual behavior. In W. C. Young (Ed.), *Sex and internal secretions,* Vol. II (ed. 3). Baltimore: Williams and Wilkins.

RADO, S. 1949 An adaptational view of sexual behavior. In P. H. Hoch and J. Zubin (Eds.), *Psychosexual development in health and disease.* New York: Grune & Stratton.

RECHY, J. 1963 *City of night.* New York: Grove Press, Inc.

REISS, A. J., JR.   1961   The social integration of queers and peers. *Soc. Prob. 9*, 102–120.

ROSS, H. L.   1959   The "hustler" in Chicago. *J. Student Research 1*, 13–19.

STRAUSS, A. L.   1959   *Mirrors and masks*. New York: Free Press.

TERMAN, L. M., AND MILES, C. C.   1936   *Sex and personality*. New York: McGraw-Hill.

WESTWOOD, G.   1960   *A minority*. London: Longmans, Green.

3

THE SEXUAL RESPONSE
CYCLE OF THE
HUMAN FEMALE

1. Gross Anatomic Considerations *

The human female's response to sexual stimulation has always been one of world literature's most popular subjects. The myriad of contributions on every aspect of the female's normal or abnormal responses to effective sexual stimulation have been a never-ending source of literary fiction and fantasy. Unfortunately, the mere popularity of the subject has led to an avalanche of pseudoscientific essays and pronouncements, which have created, in turn, an unbelievable hodgepodge of conjecture and falsehood.

Despite the subject's popularity, the earliest recorded efforts to separate a few basic anatomic and physiologic truths from this welter of misinformation were only reported as recently as the last quarter of the nineteenth century (31, 33, 37). However, during the past 50 years, important steps have been taken to create order out of this literary chaos. Havelock

* This investigation was supported in part by Research Grant RG-5998, Division of General Medical Sciences, Public Health Service.

Ellis (9) and Krafft-Ebing (28) contributed a major effort to the separating of fact from fiction. Their essentially similar technics consisted of a detailed and patient evaluation of the world's literature, and an exploitation of the information contained in their own patients' case histories. Although their fundamental concerns were primarily psychologic rather than physiologic in nature, their efforts jointly represent the first step toward objectivity in the subject of the human female's response to sexual stimulation. By no means did they always hit upon essential truth in sorting manifold opinions on every phase of the human female's sexual response cycle. Their combined efforts did create a base line or point of departure in this bigotry-burdened subject, for those who were to follow in the field.

Taking advantage of these first efforts, Dickinson (6–8) continued effective investigation in the field. He arrived at a better definition of scientific truth by the combined use of a basic-science training, and keen prowess in clinical observation. The major accomplishments in the field of scientific attempt at defining sexual response have been provided by Ford (10, 11) and Beach (2, 3). Their detailed observations of the anatomic, physiologic and psychologic responses of lower animals to sexual stimulation constitute the present authority on this subject. Many of their observations on monkey sex-behavior patterns have been of inestimable value in clarifying our own thinking and approach to the problems of the sexual reactions of the human female.

Finally, it has remained for the remarkable contributions of Kinsey, Pomeroy, Martin and Gebhard (23–26) to bring the entire subject of the human male's and female's sexual responses into the clear light of literary and scientific objectivity. Their subject coverage has concentrated upon an evaluation of the male's and female's sex drive. Our present investigative concerns are enriched by the social, economic and psychologic implications which grow from their detailed analyses of the human female's sexual responses. These implications may be effectively developed by careful interpretation of their exhaustive work. Information contained in their analytic tables will remain the best source of broadening our inadequate clinical knowledge of this subject for many years to come. One must remain in complete awe of the time-consuming effort which culminated in the publication of *Sexual Behavior in the Human Female*. As a result of this unique contribution, our own approach to the human female's sexual response cycle has not only been made plausible, but possible.

There remains one great void in our knowledge of the human female's reaction to sexual stimulation. Our information to date, objective and controlled as it has been within the power of these men to obtain and apply it, is primarily the result of individual introspection, expressed personal opinion, or of limited clinical observation, rather than a basic science approach to the sexual response cycle.

In recognition of this distinct void in our knowledge of the female's response to sexual stimulation, a program of basic science research was initiated in this field ten years ago in the Department of Obstetrics and Gynecology, Washington University School of Medicine. The express purpose of this research program is to define the human female's sexual response cycle from a scientifically objective point of view. The fundamental approaches to the human female's sexual response cycle, such as anatomy, neurology, physiology, biochemistry and endocrinology, have never been successfully defined or described. All these fields are at present under investigation as part of the program of the Reproductive Biology Research Foundation. This present report will be entirely confined to a description of the gross anatomic changes which develop during the human female's sexual response cycle. Although anatomic responses to sexual stimulation develop throughout the body, the most marked variations from the unstimulated normal are primarily confined to the breasts and pelvic organs.

In the Reproductive Biology Research Foundation, it has been found necessary to divide the human female's sexual response cycle into four arbitrary phases in order to present a more concise, anatomic picture of the transitory physical and physiologic sexual reactions. The four-part division of the sexual response cycle proposed in this paper provides a framework for more accurate and detailed description of the variations which are frequently so transient in character as to appear only in one phase of the complete orgasmic cycle. The four phases of the human female's sexual response cycle are, in order of their development: (1) the excitement phase; (2) the plateau phase; (3) the orgasmic phase; and (4) the resolution phase.

The normal excitement phase (Fig. 1, Pattern A) is initiated by any source of sexual stimulation, either of physical or psychic nature. Manipulation of any of the multiple erogenous areas of the human female's body will initiate a somatic excitement phase, just as a suggestive motion picture or pornographic literature will push the female into a psychologic excitement phase. Together with the resolution phase, the excitement phase consumes most of the time expended in the response cycle. Any variation of stimulative technics may either increase the intensity of response, thus shortening the excitement phase, or may greatly prolong or even interrupt the excitement phase, if the stimulation variant is physically irritating or psychologically objectionable.

If the source of sexual stimulation is effectively maintained, the female enters the second or plateau phase of the cycle of sexual response (Fig. 1, Pattern A). At this level the degree of sexual reaction is intense. A state of complete tumes-

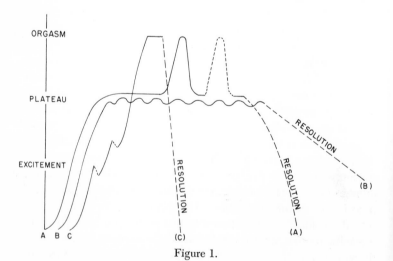

Figure 1.

cence is achieved for breasts, perineum and vagina. The female's conscious reaction to extraneous minor stimuli is frequently lost, as her body economy undergoes marked physiologic strain. This plateau phase of sexual response is the base line from which the individual climbs with relative ease and rapidity to orgasm, and is also the level to which she returns after experiencing a successful orgasmic sequence. The time variant of the plateau phase depends upon the maintenance of satisfactory sexual stimulation, regardless of its source. If effective stimulation is suddenly withdrawn, the female drops slowly from the plateau phase into a prolonged and frustrating resolution reaction.

The orgasmic phase (Fig. 1, Pattern A) of the human female's sexual response cycle is an explosive, short-term violence which may obliterate all other conscious stimuli. The superficial physical aspects of this phase of sexual response have been observed and recorded objectively (26, 34). There is no significant variation in measurable duration of the human female's orgasm, regardless of whether it is initiated by heterosexual activity or by automanipulative technics. There is, however, marked variation in the intensity of orgasmic reaction within the same subject depending upon her sexual response patterns to the stimulation of copulation, as opposed to those of manipulation. If successful stimulation technics are maintained during orgasm, or even reconstituted shortly after a successful orgasmic experience, the human female may frequently be returned from a plateau phase to a new orgasmic sequence.

The resolution phase (Fig. 1, Pattern A) has as great a time variant as its counterpart, the excitement phase, in the sexual cycle. Physiologic residuals of sex tension are slowly dissipated, and the subject returns to the normal unstimulated base line from which she departed during the excitement phase of her sexual experience. Detumescence of the sexual anatomy is completed only after all manner of sexual stimulation has been withdrawn.

As has been previously reported (5, 34, 37, 41, 42), it must be realized that there are multiple variants in the human female's sexual response cycle. Not only is there a significant difference among individual women, but there 'is also marked variation in the individual subject herself. Day to day, and week to week, she presents an entirely different picture of sexual activation for the observer.

Three different sexual response patterns have been diagrammed (Fig. 1). The patterns are only suggested response reactions, and are often altered significantly by the actively responding woman. There may be a long excitement phase with periods of purposeful delay accomplished by removal or reduction in intensity of the successful stimulation technic. Even as this "teasing technic" continues, the subject's sexual excitement will mount. With reapplication of effective stimulus, there may be relatively little or no measurable plateau phase. Instead there may be a quick, explosive jump to orgasm, followed by an equally rapid resolution phase, even ending in deep sleep within 60 to 90 seconds after such a dynamic experience in sex tension release (Fig. 1, Pattern C). On the other hand, many women may rapidly and smoothly advance through excitement to the level of the plateau phase. Here, unfortunately, they may remain in a state of complete physical and mental frustration, despite every intelligent effort to achieve orgasm. When there is no sex tension release provided by an orgasmic sequence, the resolution phase may even last for hours, particularly if some form of psychic sexual stimulation continues to exist. On occasion, detumescence of breasts and labia has taken more than 12 hours, unless sleep intervenes (Fig. 1, Pattern B).

It might be presumed, on the basis of this information, that the only relative constant phase of the sexual response cycle is that of orgasm itself. As previously indicated, its short duration and dynamic tension release is a major sensory experience. Yet, there is great variation in orgasmic intensity and in orgasmic responsiveness in the individual woman. The quick, superficial, sensory experience resulting from a three to four second orgasmic sequence is entirely different in reaction characteristic from the physiologic extreme of ten seconds of agonized physical effort, which may be produced by the ultimate in orgasmic response at the height of the individual female's sexual expression.

The technics of defining and describing the gross anatomic changes which develop during the human female's sexual response cycle have been primarily those of direct observation and physical measurement. Since the integrity of human observation of specific detail varies significantly, regardless of the observer's training or good intent, colored cinematography has been used to record in absolute detail all phases of the human sexual response cycle. The anatomic variations developed by the primary and secondary organs of reproduction, subsequent to effective sexual stimulation, have been successfully recorded by this most effective medium. It must be reemphasized that there are marked anatomic variants in response to sexual stimulation. However, certain basic anatomic reactions develop during what might be termed an average sexual response cycle. The body of this paper will be devoted to a complete description of these physical reactions.

The sexual response reactions to be described have been initiated primarily by automanipulative technics, and also by artificial and natural coition.

THE BREASTS

Excitement Phase (Fig. 2). The first response of the breasts to sexual excitement is that of erection of the nipples. This erection reaction occurs in both breasts as the result of contraction of the muscular fibers within the nipples (14). Repeated observations confirm the fact that the nipples fre-

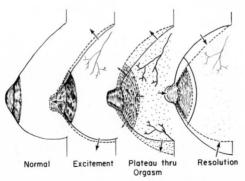

Normal   Excitement   Plateau thru   Resolution
                                Orgasm

Figure 2.

quently do not achieve full erection simultaneously. One nipple may become rapidly tumescent, while the second lags in erection rapidity and tumescent size behind the first. Inverted nipples may reverse themselves to assume a semierect position, or if the inversion is irreducible, there may be no nipple indication of the breast's reaction to sexual stimulation. The erection response may increase the nipple in length from 1.0 to 1.5 cm., and in diameter at the nipple base from 0.5 to 1 cm. over the unstimulated normal size. Large, protruding nipples do not have more capacity for relative size increase than do the essentially normal nipples. However, small nipples generally do not demonstrate a comparative size increase under stimulation. Although erection does occur, there is only a slight increase in nipple length and little, if any, increase in transverse diameter at the nipple base.

The second anatomic response in the female breasts (during the excitement phase) is that of a marked increase in definition of venous pattern. This engorgement of the venous pattern may first be seen over the anterior superior surfaces of the breasts and, depending upon breast size, is occasionally well-defined on the inferior breast surfaces. A satisfactory rule of thumb is to expect the most definitive increase in venous pattern from the larger breasts. Frequently the typical bluish pattern of increased vasocongestion is quite conspicuous over the anterior chest wall, before attaining prominence on the anterior surfaces of the breasts. Engorgement of the vascular tree rarely extends centrally as far as the areola, since there is fairly rapid drainage to the axillary veins (40). As the excitement phase progresses toward plateau, there is a marked increase in actual breast size as the result of the organs' marked vasocongestive reaction. With the woman in a standing position, this breast fullness is more easily visualized in the lower half of a pendulous breast. Tumescence of the whole breast with sexual excitement was first described by Dickinson (7).

Plateau Phase (Fig. 2). A marked engorgement occurs in the areolae of the breasts during the terminal stages of the excitement phase. As plateau progresses, the areolae become so tumescent in appearance that they impinge upon the erect nipples. The impression is created that the nipple has lost its erection. Actually this is a false impression, as we shall learn during the resolution phase. Before the female leaves the plateau phase in the final surge toward orgasm, the breasts have increased in size from a fifth to a quarter over the individual's own norm. The virginal breast (the breast that has never been suckled) usually demonstrates more distensive ability than the previously suckled breast. It is apparent that the increase in breast size with sexual excitement is not only the result of the vasocongestive reaction previously described, but may also be effectively aided by fibrous tissue elements which invest the breast lobules as supportive aids (40).

Repeated observation has created the impression that the more pendulous and slack the breasts, the more resistant the breasts to the vasocongestive reaction of sexual excitement. With previous milk distention, significant supportive structure damage occurs in the breasts. In addition, there remains a hypertrophied venous drainage pattern when the previously nursed breast is compared to the virginal breast. Thus it is that, although the vasocongestive reaction may be just as severe in different subjects, the breasts' ability to react to this congestive mechanism by obvious tumescence is distinctly marred by an established state of parity. Particularly is this true if the individual has either nursed without effective breast support, or has experienced a severe breast engorgement reaction during the immediate postpartum period.

As the subject rises from excitement to the plateau phase, a pink mottling frequently appears over the anterior, lateral and ultimately the inferior surfaces of the breasts. Actually, this papillary rash first appears over the epigastrium, and spreads to the breast surfaces as the plateau phase is firmly established. This spotty flush actually coalesces in the terminal stages of the plateau phase, to suggest to the observer an advanced state of measles. The flush phenomenon will be described in more detail in the following section of the paper.

Orgasmic Phase (Fig. 2). There is no distinct breast reaction to the experience of orgasm. The nipples are erect, although tumescence of the areolae gives the impression of a significant reduction in the erection reaction. The areolar tumescence does not progress beyond the reaction maturity established early in the plateau phase. The vascular tree stands out in bold relief, and the breasts are a fifth to a quarter increased in size. They appear quite heavy, pendulous, and in the erect position become quite tremulous, due to the increase in size and weight as the body goes through the spasm of orgasm.

Resolution Phase (Fig. 2). The first resolution phase activity is loss of the measle-like mottled flush over the breast surfaces. Following shortly, or occasionally occurring coincidentally, is detumescence of the areolae. The nipples again become obviously erect. The observer has the impression that the source of sexual stimulation is continuing, or that the nipples are reacting to a renewed stimulation effect by becoming repeatedly erect. This "false erection" reaction is simply the result of early detumescence of the grossly engorged areolae before the nipple erection reaction subsides. The breasts lose their increased size slowly, as a general rule. There is frequently a retained increase in total breast volume which lasts from five to ten minutes after the orgasmic phase has been terminated. One of the last of the sexual excitement stigmata to retrogress is the engorged venous pattern. Frequently, the nipples undergo complete involution before the venous pattern returns to its normal, ill-defined state. This persistence of vasocongestion, particularly in the nonparous breast, may well be the result of the gross overdistention of the circulus venosus of Haller (14) during the plateau phase with resultant slowed venous drainage into the internal mammary venous plexus.

VASCULAR FLUSH PHENOMENON

The protean character of the vascular flush reaction to effective sexual stimulation has not been previously described. With the aid of artificially-increased skin surface temperature, such as that necessary for successful motion-picture photography, the wide distribution of this flush becomes quite apparent. Of course, the intensity of the reaction varies among individuals. However, for some the flush reaction is a direct indication of the degree of sexual stimulation achieved. This papillary-type of erythematous rash first appears over the epigastrium in the late stages of the excitement phase, or shortly after the plateau phase has been achieved. The flush then spreads rapidly over the breasts, first appearing on the anterior and superior surfaces, and the anterior chest wall. In order, the lateral and medial breast surfaces become involved. Finally, the extension of the flush is frequently noted on the undersurfaces of the breasts, or orgasm is imminent.

The vascular reaction to sex tension is not confined to the organs of sexual response. Most of the body surfaces of reactive subjects respond during the plateau phase of the sexual cycle. The flush may be seen spreading over the lower abdomen, the shoulders, even the antecubital fossae bilaterally, as sexual tension mounts. With orgasm imminent, this measle-like rash has been observed to spread over the anterior-lateral borders of the thighs, the buttocks and the whole back.

The sex-tension flush reaches its peak to terminate with the explosion of orgasm. The strained, flushed features of the human female as she reaches for orgasmic relief have been well described (5, 11, 23, 26, 41). It is now evident that the vascular flush described for the face and anterior chest wall has complete body distribution, spreading, in susceptible subjects, in direct proportion to the intensity of the orgasm. There is not sufficient evidence at this time to warrant a statement of incidence of the vascular flush phenomenon in the general female population during the sexual response cycle.

Resolution of the flush reaction occurs coincidentally with the appearance of a filmy, generalized perspiration reaction. Many women have described a sensation of either being excessively warm (sweaty), or feeling cold, as they retreat from orgasm into the resolution phase. A perspiration response to effective sexual stimulation has been described frequently during the last 30 years (9, 34, 38, 44). The physiologic background of its sexual cycle appearance has not been previously understood. The filmy perspiration is distributed over the back, thighs and chest wall as the woman recovers conscious interest in her surroundings. Frequently, perspiration runs from the axillae and can be noticed as a superficial surface coating of the entire body, from the shoulders to thighs. A marked perspiration reaction may also be noted on the forehead and upper lip of women whose faces have been mottled in the usual patchy manner by a flush reaction, as orgasm approached.

There is no apparent relationship between the fine, filmy perspiration covering the trunk and face during the resolution phase of the vascular phenomenon, and the degree of physical activity associated with the successful climb from plateau phase to orgasm itself. One observed subject, undergoing electroencephalographic evaluation, had been trained for four months to attain orgasm without producing concomitant muscle tension, in order to provide significance for her tracing patterns. Yet, this woman repeatedly showed a marked flush phenomenon over the entire body during plateau and orgasm, and during resolution was completely covered with a filmy, fine perspiration. Her actual physical activity, as recorded by the electroencephalogram, was essentially negligible in this particular situation. These evidences of a strained, physiologic body economy, independent of physical effort or initiation, are undergoing further objective evaluation.

The order in which the flush reaction disappears from the body is almost in direct reversal of the sequence of appearance on different body sites. The papillary rash disappears quickly over the back and buttocks, the lower abdomen, arms and thighs. It is much slower to disappear over the breasts, but finally resolves from the breasts before complete disappearance from its primary source over the epigastrium. The perspiration reaction appearing simultaneously over all body sites is the first indication of the resolution phase in the sexual response cycle. The breasts may be covered with perspiration, and still demonstrate the last disappearing vestiges of the vascular flush phenomenon. The degree of persistence of the perspiration coating of the body surfaces obviously depends on the opportunities for evaporation and/or absorption by clothing or bedding materials.

THE EXTERNAL GENITALIA (Figs. 3, 4, 5, 6 and 7)

The *clitoris* undergoes specific anatomic changes during the course of the female's sexual response cycle, as detailed in Chapter 4.

The labia majora respond to sexual stimulation in direct relation to the parity of the subject. In the nullipara, as the sexual stimulation progresses, the major labia thin out and flatten against the perineum. There is also a slight elevation of the labia in an upward and outward direction away from the vaginal outlet. This may simply be the anatomic result of protrusion of the labia minora and engorgement of the terminal vagina. This flattening and anterolateral displacement of the major labia is usually completed before the plateau phase is achieved. In essence, this is an anatomic reaction to increasing sexual tension. It is an involuntary attempt to remove any impediment from the shortly anticipated "mounting-process." There is no change in anatomy for the labia majora during the plateau or orgasmic phase. During the terminal stages of resolution, the labia return to normal thickness and positioning. In instances of a subject's repetitive return to excitement or plateau phases, the labia majora may become quite engorged and edematous, and frequently persist in this state for several hours during a protracted resolution phase.

In the multiparous individual (particularly the individual with significant labial varicosity involvement), the labia majora become markedly engorged during the excitement phase. Instead of flattening in an anterolateral elevation reaction against the female perineum, the labia majora have been observed during the plateau phase to become two to three times increased in size. If this size increase occurs, there is no elevating or flattening of the labia against the perineum. The labia continue in normal position as a pendulous, swollen curtain. There is usually a marked gaping of the vaginal outlet in these individuals, so that the vasocongested labia majora do not interfere with the normal "mounting-process." This type of marked vascular engorgement in a varicosity-distressed individual may persist through the resolution phase for two to three hours before complete detumescence has been achieved.

One female, with an exceptionally gaping outlet as the result of obstetrical trauma, successfully carried coitus to the stage of complete expenditure of male partners 27 times over an observed 6½-hour period. The large major labia hung lateral to the outlet in thickened folds (at least three times normal size) but were successfully positioned (by the obstetrical trauma) to remove the possibility of any local mechanical irritation, which might have been theoretically associated with the repeated coital efforts. Kept in a constant excitement phase and reporting five instances of plateau achievement during this prolonged sexual effort, the woman nonetheless failed to obtain orgasmic relief. Her resolution phase was even more prolonged than her sexual experience. The breasts did not return to essentially normal size for 1 hour and 20 minutes. The labia majora were still obviously engorged and swollen 6 hours after her last coital effort.

It was particularly interesting to note the continued state of engorgement of the labia and the outer third of the vagina over a long period of continued observation. This persistent vasocongestive reaction was distressing enough to prevent sleep. As soon as the six-hour postorgasmic observation period was declared terminated, the subject sought immediate relief from this long-continued irritative, vasocongestive reaction by an automanipulative orgasm. With violent, sexual tension release (accomplished in just under two minutes), the labial congestion completely disappeared within fifteen minutes. All physical symptoms of the vasocongestive distress were released with the attainment of an effective orgasmic experience.

Genital pain associated with maintained sexual excitement has been described in the literature occasionally (16, 29, 34, 45). The mechanism of the pelvic pain response has not been understood previous to the observations of the state of long-continued unresolved vasocongestion just described. The pain response is produced by the severe unresolved vasocongestion of the primary organs of sexual response.

The labia minora undergo startling changes during the sexual response cycle. There are vivid color variations which remind one particularly of the color changes of the sex-skin of the female monkey in estrus (46). During the excitement phase of the human sexual response cycle, the labia minora (sex-skin) turn bright pink in color and, as sexual tension mounts, engorge to approximately twice their previously normal size. During terminal stages of the excitement phase or early in plateau levels of sexual response, the vivid "sex-skin" color is altered from the pink of excitement to a deeper scarlet-red hue. This "sex-skin" color change is in direct proportion to the degree of sexual tension obtained by the subject under observation. The multipara, with normally increased vaso-congestion of the perineal area, may frequently develop a color change so marked that, as her plateau phase continues, there may be noted a deep purplish-red or burgundy color of the labia minora. In many observed instances, subjects have progressed far in the excitement phase, or even attained a satisfactory plateau level of sexual response, but have been unable to achieve orgasmic tension release. These women will show only the bright pink, tell-tale color of the excitement phase response to sexual tension. Of major interest, however, is the fact that no observed individual has attained a plateau phase with the "sex-skin" turning either the nulliparous brilliant red, or the occasional multiparous burgundy color, without then attaining a most satisfactory orgasmic response.

It has become evident with repetitive observation that the "sex-skin" (labia minora) provides a reasonably satisfactory, gross clinical measurement of the degree of sexual tension achieved by a woman, and ultimately of the effectiveness of the tension release mechanism. If the bright pink of the excitement phase changes to a brilliant primiparous scarlet-red, or the multiparous burgundy color, a satisfactory plateau phase has been achieved. A successful orgasmic sequence is sure to follow if sexual stimulation is continued without interruption. During the resolution phase, the tension colors of the "sex-skin" quickly return to the light pink of an early excitement phase response. This "sex-skin" color alteration from the brilliant red or burgundy color of plateau reaction level back to the light excitement phase pink is generally concluded within 90 to 120 seconds after orgasm. The change from the excitement phase pink to the normally unstimulated perineal color is also relatively rapid, but does not occur with such uniform regularity. The "sex-skin" undergoing a terminal resolution reaction has quite a blotchy appearance as it is in the process of returning to normal color levels. The total resolution phase of the "sex-skin" color alterations is usually completed within five minutes of the termination of the actual orgasmic experience.

When the labia minora have achieved the color of plateau or imminent orgasmic phase, they are at least twice normal size. Together with the vasocongested outer third of the vagina, they form an engorged central vaginal axis in an involuntary attempt to grasp the shaft of the penis. The labia minora become so congested that they actually add a full centimeter to the functional length of the vagina by helping to provide a supportive platform for the shaft of the penis. Their own engorged weight provides a slight involuntary gaping of the vaginal outlet even in the nullipara. This "mounting-invitation" is usually less obvious in a nullipara with the normal, high perineum and small fourchette. The multipara with the usual gaping vaginal outlet of a late excitement or early plateau phase demonstrates, with the aid of the engorged minor labia, a most obvious "mounting-invitation" reaction.

BARTHOLIN GLANDS

The presumed role of the Bartholin glands in the human female's sexual response cycle has been described in great detail by multiple investigators during the past half century (5, 19, 32, 36, 41, 43–45). It has been generally agreed that the function of these glands is to provide sufficient lubrication for successful and painless vaginal penetration. The appearance at the fourchette of secretory material presumably produced by the Bartholin glands has been taken as a very early sign of response to sexual stimulation. Repeated observations have failed to confirm these views.

Certainly it is true that the Bartholin glands do respond to sexual stimulation by secretory activity. However, this secretory action is rarely demonstrable until late in the excitement phase or even early in the plateau levels. Additionally, the secretory activity is usually confined to a mere droplet of a mucoid-appearing material, particularly in the nulliparous subject. The multipara may show a slight increase in secretory activity of the Bartholin glands, but under observation there has never been sufficient secretory material produced to accomplish more than the minimal lubrication of the vaginal fourchette.

The basis of all vaginal lubrication comes from the vaginal walls themselves. This lubrication phenomenon appears early in the excitement phase of sexual response. The production of this material is in such copious quantity in the normally-responding individual, that the vaginal outlet is quickly and effectively lubricated. In essence then, the secretory activity of the Bartholin glands is a negligible factor in the complete picture of vaginal or even introital lubrication. In addition, the late appearance of the Bartholin's secretory material in the female's response cycle also rules out its role as that of a primary lubricating mechanism.

Bartholin gland secretions have also been assigned the role of reducing vaginal acidity to provide greater sperm longevity (19, 44). The late appearance of the secretory material in the sexual response cycle would lend substance to this concept from a timing point of view alone. However, the secretory material is so minute in amount when compared to the total vaginal secretory activity, that the concept is mechanically and chemically impossible. It is true that there is a change in recordable vaginal acidity during the complete sexual response cycle; but this change in vaginal acidity is the direct result of the vaginal lubrication phenomenon, and not that of Bartholin gland secretory activity.

URETHRA AND URINARY BLADDER

Observation of the urethra during repeated orgasmic cycles has shown occasional, involuntary spreading of the external meatus. This dilatation of the meatus is a minimal reaction; occurs with no established regularity; nor with any observed direct relationship to orgasmic intensity. There was no involuntary loss of urine observed in any sexual response cycle.

Several subjects reported the urge to void after successful completion of a heterosexually stimulated orgasmic cycle. The urge to void during or immediately after cohabitation has been previously reported (9, 13, 17, 44). The individuals who had the urge to void during intercourse had, in each instance, the primiparous type of high, firm perineum and diminished vaginal outlet. These nulliparous anatomic structures combined to direct and hold the penis along the anterior vaginal wall and thus, reflexly irritated the posterior wall of the urinary bladder. Only in this particular type of woman was bladder tenesmus described as a coital or postcoital complication.

There have been two women who described minimal loss of urine during heights of sexual excitement. In both instances advanced cystourethroceles were present. These two women also reported frequent, involuntary urine escapage with the acts of coughing or sneezing. Both were able to maintain continence without difficulty (despite the fact that there was measurable residual urine in the bladder), if they voided immediately before any type of developed sexual excitement.

This admittedly inadequate experience tends to support the contention that the genitourinary system does not contribute to the popular conception of a female ejaculation response to sexual excitement (9, 13, 44). Those who lost urinary control were well aware of this occurrence, and positive in their own minds of the origin of the fluid loss.

THE VAGINA (Fig. 3)

The normal anatomic reactions within the vagina during the various phases of the human female's sexual response cycle have been successfully recorded in color motion-picture photography. In addition, the anatomic variations from basically normal patterns have been defined by direct observation of over 1000 complete vaginal orgasmic cycles. Subjects have met the usual research control demands of varying age groupings, parity and menstrual cycle timings. The multiple vaginal alterations are reported in relation to the different phases of the sexual response cycle, following the technics established

Normal

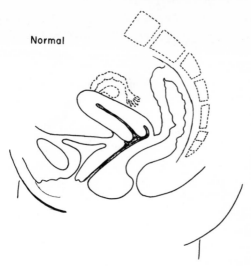

Figure 3.

for the anatomic consideration of the breast reactions. Again, as with the breasts, many of the anatomic variations seen in the vagina during the complete sexual response cycle are confined to one or even two of the response phases, and are not constantly present throughout the entire sexual cycle.

Excitement Phase (Fig. 4A). The first anatomic evidence of the excitement phase response appears on the walls of the vagina within a matter of 30 seconds after the initiation of somatic or psychic sexual stimulation. This first and almost immediate response to effective sexual stimulation is the phenomenon of vaginal lubrication. In the past there have been innumerable efforts to describe the source of the vaginal lubrication which obviously develops with mounting sex tension. Over the years, the cervix has been considered the main source of vaginal lubrication by many authors (1, 4, 5, 7, 9, 26, 30, 34, 39, 42–44). Bartholin glands, as previously described, have also been allotted a major role in the production of vaginal lubrication. Neither the healthy cervix nor the Bartholin glands make any essential contribution to the development of vaginal lubrication.

Excitement

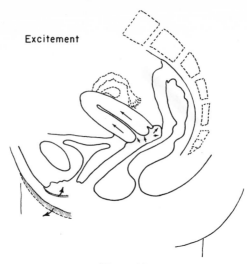

Figure 4A.

As response to sexual tension develops, a "sweating-phenomenon" may be observed developing on the vaginal walls. Individual droplets of a transudate-like material appear scattered throughout the rugal folds of the normal vaginal architecture. These individual droplets, which appear within ten to thirty seconds of onset of sexual stimulation, present a picture somewhat akin to that of a "perspiration-beaded" fore-head. With mounting tension, the droplets coalesce to form a smooth, glistening coating for the entire vaginal wall. This "sweating-phenomenon" progresses to establish complete vaginal lubrication early in the excitement phase of the human female's sexual response. The lubrication reaction, as it spreads along the vaginal walls, is certainly the first evidence of vaginal response to effective sexual stimulation. This unique "sweating-phenomenon" may be initiated by psychic sexual, as well as somatic sexual stimulation. The simple technic of providing subjects with pornographic material to read while the vagina is under direct observation soon produces a most successful vaginal lubrication reaction.

The observation of this vaginal "sweating-phenom-enon" has been one of the most interesting aspects of the gross anatomic study of the human female's sexual response cycle. Present information suggests that this transudate-like material is the result of a marked dilation of the venous plexus concentration which encircles the entire barrel of the vagina. The bulbus vestibuli, plexus pudendalis, plexus uterovaginalis and, questionably, the plexus vesicalis and plexus hemorrhoidalis externus are all involved in a fulminating vasocongestive reaction along the walls of the vagina. Apparently, from this great vasocongestive reaction, the transudate-like material develops to lubricate the vagina. It has long been established that there are essentially no glandular elements in the walls of the vagina (30). Yet this transudate-like material appears readily, usually in copious amounts, early in the excitement phase of the sexual response cycle. The biochemical details of the nature of the lubricating material, together with its effect upon normal vaginal chemistry will be presented in a subsequent paper.

Complete lack of cervical gland secretory activity during sexual excitement has been noted in over 1000 direct observations of the entire sexual response cycle. In only one instance was any cervical activity of a secretory nature noted. In this particular instance, a mucous plug was lost from the cervical outlet under direct observation. The woman was in the thirteenth day of a regularly recurring 28-day menstrual cycle. It was interesting to note that although this thin, ovulatory-type mucus was extruded from the cervical canal, the reaction occurred late in the plateau phase of the sexual response cycle, long after complete vaginal lubrication had been achieved.

There are two other pieces of information which should be presented while on this subject of the problem of the lack of cervical secretory contribution to vaginal lubrication. First, a pronounced "sweating-phenomenon" has been observed in women who have had a complete hysterectomy and bilateral salpingo-oophorectomy. The ability of these women to lubricate with reasonable effectiveness, even in a completely panhysterectomized state, mechanically eliminates the cervix from significant consideration as a primary lubricating source. In other cases, a surgically and mechanically created artificial vagina also has been visualized during an entire sexual response cycle. The artificial vaginal walls develop effective lubrication following the pattern of the "sweating-phenomenon" reaction. In these instances also there are no Bartholin glands available to the external genitalia, and certainly no cervix in the artificially created vaginal canal. In summation, one may conclude that cervical secretory activity, so frequently described as a constant reaction during the human female's sexual response cycle, is a nonexistent entity.

As the excitement phase continues, additional secondary responses develop within the vagina. Initially, there is a lengthening and distention of the inner two-thirds of the vaginal barrel. As sexual tension mounts towards the plateau phase, irregular, convulsive, expansive movements of the vaginal walls may be observed. During the excitement phase the entire vagina is markedly dilated or dilatable, but this expansion-type reaction is confined to the inner two-thirds of the vagina. This area expands spasmodically with directed force, and then relaxes in a slow, tensionless, irregular manner.

In addition to the expansive effort of the vaginal fornices, the cervix and corpus are pulled slowly back and up into the false pelvis or lower abdomen, as sexual tension mounts. This reaction, together with the dilation of the fornices, obviously contributes greatly to the distention or distensibility of the inner two-thirds of the vaginal barrel. The slow, irregular elevation of the cervix back and up into the lower abdomen depends upon the uterus resting in its usual anterior position in a sexually unstimulated state. If the uterus is in marked third degree retroversion, for example, not only is there no cervical movement out of the usual vaginal axis, but the normal lateral excursion and posterior expansion of the vaginal fornices are also markedly reduced.

In order to visualize the distensive ability of the vaginal barrel during the excitement phase, it must be recalled that anatomically the vagina is a potential, rather than an actual space. Unless a menstrual period is in progress, or some minimal degree of continued sexual tension exists, the anterior and posterior walls of the vagina are essentially in complete apposition. Thus, it is evident that the minimal spacing left

NORMAL

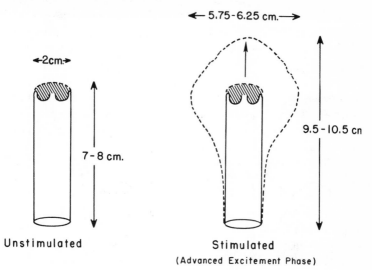

Figure 4B.

between the anterior and posterior vaginal walls in the draw-ing simulating normal pelvic anatomy (Fig. 3) is in truth, poetic license. Despite the collapsed state of the unstimulated vagina, it has long been obvious that the normal vagina is infinitely distensible (from a purely clinical point of view).

The nulliparous, sexually unstimulated vagina (Fig. 4B) has been repetitively measured at a 2 cm. lateral wall distention, just anterior to the resting, normally-placed cervix. As sexual tension mounts, lateral wall distention ranges from 5.75 to 6.25 cm. The vaginal length (fourchette to posterior fornix wall) of the unstimulated, nulliparous vagina has varied in different subjects from 7 to 8 cm. With sexual stimulation the vaginal length measurement increases to 9.5 to 10.5 cm.

In an attempt to demonstrate the vagina's essentially unlimited clinical distensibility, the same lateral vaginal wall and vaginal length measurements were taken with nulliparous vaginae previously distended by indwelling specula (Fig. 4C).

SPECULUM DILATED

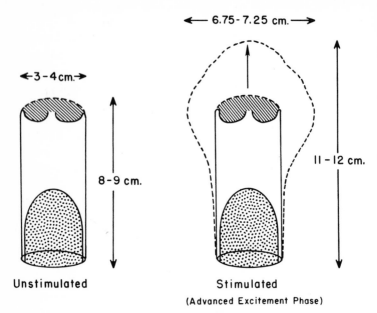

Figure 4C.

The specula were placed at a fixed dilation of 2 cm. between the anterior and posterior blades. The initial lateral wall distention readings were now an average of 3 to 4 cm., and vaginal length was recorded at an 8 to 9 cm. average. With an established excitement phase, the lateral vaginal walls reached distention averages of 6.75 to 7.25 cm., and vaginal length figures were recorded at an 11 to 12 cm. average.

It is obvious from these figures that the more the vagina dilates, the more further dilation becomes possible. When we compare the two sets of figures the diagrams provide, we see an average increase of 3.75 to 4.25 cm. in width, and 2.5 cm. in length for the unstimulated normal vagina. When the vagina is partially dilated by an indwelling speculum, the width increase under the influence of effective sexual stimulation is 3.75 to 4.25 cm., and the length increase averages 3 cm. From these essentially similar figures it is obvious that the inner two-thirds of the vagina expands, and the vagina lengthens under sexual stimulation with complete disregard of a previously established distention state.

This experiment was not repeated with multiparous subjects. The previously over-distended and obstetrically traumatized vaginae of the multiparous subjects did not provide a satisfactory norm from which to measure significant vaginal distensibility other than on an individual basis. On this basis, however, the statement can still be made that regardless of the advanced degree of established lateral wall distension or length measurements, the multiparous vagina will increase significantly in its length and lateral wall measurable distensibility under effective sexual stimulation.

During the excitement phase, the vaginal walls also undergo a distinct color alteration. The normal, purplish-red coloring of the endocrinologically well-stimulated vaginal rugal pattern slowly develops the darker, deeper, purplish hue of vasocongestion. This purple discoloration is patchy in character during the early stages of the excitement phase, but as the plateau level is achieved and the vaginal vasocongestion becomes intense, the entire vaginal barrel perceptively darkens in appearance.

There is also a flattening of the rugal pattern of the well-stimulated vaginal wall. This occurs as expansion reactions of the vaginal fornices progress during the excitement phase. This thinning of the vaginal mucosa is obviously a corollary of the expansion efforts of the inner two-thirds of the vagina.

Plateau Phase (Fig. 5). The anatomic alterations of the vagina subsequent to sexual stimulation are not confined to the inner two-thirds of the vaginal barrel. The outer third of the vagina dilates modestly during the sexual excitement phase (2.5 to 3.0 cm. average). However, the primary responses of the outer third of the vagina are confined to the plateau and orgasmic phases of sexual response. With the onset of plateau phase response, a marked vasocongestion occurs within the walls of the vaginal canal. The entire outer third of the vagina, including the bulbocavernosus muscle

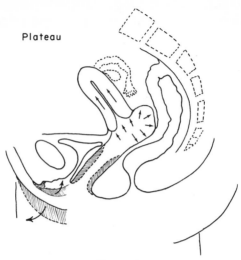

Figure 5.

area becomes grossly distended with venous blood. This distention is so marked that the central lumen of the vagina is reduced by approximately a third over what has previously been noted during the excitement phase. The constriction of the central lumen of the vagina, subsequent to excessive vasocongestion of the outer third of the vaginal wall, is the mechanism which contributes to the feeling of gripping or tightening about the shaft of the penis as the female approaches her orgasm during heterosexual activity. Although this outer-third vaginal canal vasodistention is apparently quite involuntary, it is a sure indication that the plateau level of the sexual response cycle has been achieved. The broad base of vasocongestion which encompasses the entire outer third of the vagina, together with the engorged labia minora, provides an anatomic platform for the vagina's mechanical expression of orgasm.

There is a minimal further increase in depth and width of the vagina (measured at the fornices), which occurs during the plateau phase. This is a negligible degree of enlargement over the previous levels established during the excitement phase. The degree of reaction is not standardized; so it was not measured objectively. At this stage of vaginal plateau reaction, the "sex-skin" (labia minora) has turned to a primiparous scarlet-red or occasional multiparous burgundy color, so significant of impending orgasm. In addition, the engorged labia minora, together with the markedly vasodistended outer third of the vagina, develop a funnel or canal to direct the penis in a "mounting-reaction."

The vaginal lubrication phenomenon, reaching completion during the excitement phase, shows no further change either with plateau levels, or the achievement of orgasm.

Orgasm Phase (Fig. 6). With orgasm the expansion of the inner two-thirds of the vagina is no more advanced or spasmodic than during the terminal stages of the excitement phase. The basic force direction is still expansive, however, rather than constrictive in character.

There is a completely characteristic physical reaction occurring in the outer third of the vagina which is restricted to the orgasmic phase of the sexual response cycle. The broad-based platform that the vasodistention reaction has provided

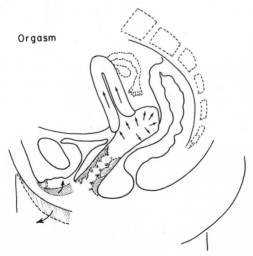

Figure 6.

in the outer third of the vagina during the plateau phase, contracts strongly with a regularly recurring pattern during the orgasmic phase. The contractions occur at roughly one-second intervals, and recur from a minimum of three to four, up to a maximum of ten times with each individual's orgasmic experience. Direct observation of the anatomic mechanism behind the orgasmic contraction response in the outer third of the vagina provides an adequate explanation for the vaginal spasm or penile grasping reaction, that has been described in general terms so many times in the literature (1, 4, 7, 9, 17, 19, 27, 29, 32, 35, 36, 37, 43, 44).

The generalized response to orgasm is an involuntary contraction of the entire perineal body, the outer third of the vagina, the rectum, and the lower abdomen. The transverse perinei muscles, superficial and deep, the bulbocavernosus grouping bilaterally, the sphincter ani external, and the lower portion of the rectus abdominus are the muscles of primary response. The levator ani and the ischiocavernosus muscles bilaterally contribute secondarily to the involuntary contractions of the entire perineal body, and to the plateau phase platform developed in the outer one-third of the vaginal barrel. In addition to local anatomic response, there is also a general pelvic reaction. As the woman experiences her orgasm, the entire pelvis is spasmodically and irregularly elevated from the usual horizontal plane in a pleasure response.

The duration of the orgasmic contraction ring's regularly recurring spastic response in the outer third of the vagina, and the severity of the contraction excursion into the central lumen of the vagina, varies from subject to subject. Individual subject variation is also constantly noted. The intensity of any particular orgasm depends upon a number of variables such as present position in the menstrual month, excessive or unusual fatigue, illness, unusually hot weather, alcoholic intake, or a recently experienced orgasmic reaction. Work is now in progress to define the influence of these many variables upon the actual intensity of the orgasmic contraction ring response to effective sexual stimulation. This spasmodic contraction of the outer third of the vagina is the only significant physical response reaction which is purely confined to the orgasmic phase.

Resolution Phase (Fig. 7). With onset of the resolution phase, the first retrogressive changes occur in the outer third of the vagina. The vasodistention reaction which was established during the plateau phase, and which (together with the engorged "sex-skin") served as a springboard for the telltale spasmodic contractions of orgasm, is rapidly dispersed. As the result of this rapid loss of localized vasocongestion, the central lumen of the outer third of the vagina actually increases in its diameter in the early phases of the resolution reaction. The anatomic similarity between the rapid detumescence of the orgasmic platform in the outer third of the vagina, and detumescence of the penis after ejaculation is so striking that this postorgasmic correlation between the two sexes must be mentioned in passing.

Slowly the expanded inner two-thirds of the vagina shrinks back to the collapsed, unstimulated state. This is not a direct or suddenly completed collapse of the vaginal walls. It is rather an irregular, spotty, zonal type of relaxation re-

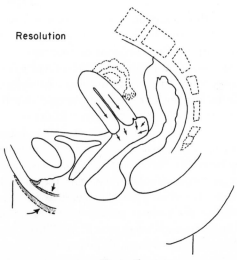

Resolution

Figure 7.

action, which slowly drops the cervix of the normally an-
teriorly-positioned uterus back into the depth of the vagina
from its excitement phase positioning in the false pelvis. This
slow relaxation places the cervix in correct position to enter a
theoretically-obtained seminal pool in the depth of the vagina.
The return of the cervix to the vaginal axis from its elevated
position in the lower abdomen, and the coordinated collapse
of the vaginal fornices frequently takes at least three to four
minutes to complete after orgasm has been experienced. This
reaction points out the importance of correct positioning in
intercourse for infertile couples, particularly if there is a problem of poor sperm production.

The usual deep-purple vaginal mucosal color changes
of the plateau and orgasmic phases return to basic coloration
in a slow retrogressive process, which frequently takes as long
as ten to fifteen minutes. Normal rugal patterns, so typical of
the humorally well-stimulated vaginal wall, become more apparent as the expansive reaction of the inner two-thirds of the
vagina, and the venous distention of the outer third of the
vagina retrogress toward the unstimulated normal.

THE CERVIX

Some of the anatomic reactions of the cervix to the
stimulation of the sexual response cycle have necessarily been
described in detail in other sections of this paper, to provide
continuity for the general picture. The cervix rises (with a
normal, anteriorly-placed corpus) into the false pelvis or lower
abdomen, as sexual tension mounts during the latter stages
of the excitement phase. This upward withdrawal movement
toward the center of the false pelvis is accomplished by the
entire corpus, simultaneously with the advanced expansion reaction of the inner two-thirds of the vagina. The impression is
created that Mackenrodt's ligaments are the primary source
of support used to accomplish this cervical movement. The
irregular bulbus enlargement of the posterior fornix of the
vagina also suggests sacrouterine activity. These assumptions
have not been satisfactorily established to date.

The lack of secretory activity of the normally healthy
cervix during any part of the sexual response cycle has been

described in the section of this report dealing with vaginal lubrication. In brief, it may be unequivocally stated that the cervix is in no way connected with, or responsible for the phenomenon of vaginal lubrication. Thus, the concept of an ejaculation by the female partner, which has occasionally been described in the literature, may safely be denied (9, 13, 44).

During the plateau and orgasmic phases of sexual response, there is only one specific anatomic reaction of the cervix. A slight patulousness of the external cervical os develops immediately after the orgasmic release of sexual tension. This cervical reaction lasts through the first five to ten minutes of the resolution phase before returning to normal. If obstetrical trauma has provided lacerations and/or scar tissue about the external cervical os, the gaping reaction usually cannot be demonstrated.

The gaping of the external cervical os has been assigned the anatomic function of aiding sperm passage (7, 12, 39, 45). If there is any anatomic aid to sperm passage provided by the slight patulousness of the external os at orgasm, it is purely passive in character. The cervix and the thin cervical mucus of ovulatory density may well present a sponge effect for an effectively placed seminal pool in the depth of the vagina, but there is no anatomic reaction to aid in sperm uptake, such as a sucking effect at the external cervical os with orgasm. The "sucking-reaction" of the uterus combined with a patulous cervix, has been described repeatedly in the literature (7, 9, 12, 15, 18–22, 27, 29, 36, 42, 43, 45). Suffice it to say at this time that this effect has not been confirmed at the Reproductive Biology Research Foundation using automanipulative technics to achieve female orgasmic sexual response. Experimental proof of this statement will be provided in a report dealing with the physiology of the uterine sexual response.

Slight, patchy, purplish color changes have been observed on the surface of the multiparous or chronically infected or eroded cervix during the latter stages of the plateau phase of sexual response. These color changes are by no means as well-defined as those of the vagina, nor do they appear in the same subject with any established consistency.

THE UTERUS

The reactions of the uterus to effective sexual stimulation will not be considered at this time. These reactions, primarily physiologic in character, vary among nulliparous, multiparous and pregnant uteri. The results of detailed physiologic evaluation of uteri in both pregnant and nonpregnant states, with multiple variations in response to sexual stimulation, will be published in a separate paper in the near future.

THE PERINEUM

During the sexual response cycle the only anatomic changes noted in relation to the perineum are a spasmodic tightening of the perineal body during the terminal plateau phase as orgasm is approached, and involuntary, irregular elevation of the entire perineum as orgasm is experienced. The first reaction is, of course, much better defined by the nulliparous perineum than by that of the multipara, unless an adequate episiotomy and good perineal repair have been sustained. Spasmodic constriction of the perineal body as a terminal plateau and orgasmic phase response may not be demonstrable with the typical, gaping, multiparous introitus. If a significant rectocele is present, perineal constriction has not been observed to occur.

The only constant perineal color change noted during the sexual response cycle has been noted on the fourchette. Here the early, bright-pink reaction of the excitement phase frequently turns a scarlet red or even a burgundy color during the plateau phase, if multiparous varicosities lend increased vascularity to the perineal body.

THE RECTUM

The only response of the rectum to normal sexual stimulation is active contraction of the rectal sphincter with orgasm. This reaction does not constantly occur during orgasm. It is, however, a significant indication of the intensity of the orgasm. During the more intense, well-developed five to ten second type of orgasmic response, when extensive contraction occurs in the outer third of the vagina, the rectal sphincter may contract with spastic regularity. In short, the contraction of orgasm described for the outer third of the vagina is also frequently carried out simultaneously by the perineal body and the external rectal sphincter. This type of reaction is particularly true for the orgasm elicited by automanipulation, but it also occasionally occurs with coitus.

SKELETAL MUSCLE AND ORGANS OF SPECIAL SENSE

The detailed anatomic descriptions of the human female's reaction to sexual stimulation have been essentially confined in this report, as previously indicated, to the primary and secondary organs of sexual response. There are numerous partial, and relatively adequate descriptions of voluntary and involuntary reactions of skeletal muscles and organs of special sense to effective sexual stimulation (1, 7, 9, 11, 32, 37–39, 43). The most accurate descriptions of the body elements' reactions to increasing sexual tension may be found reported in sufficient detail by Kinsey and his coworkers (26), and by Negri (34). Since our information is in essential agreement with their generalized, gross anatomic description of other than the organs of special sense, there is nothing to be gained by repetitive literary exercise. The responses of the organs of special sense to effective sexual stimulation will be the subject of future reports.

DISCUSSION

It is obvious from the detailed descriptions of the anatomy of sexual response presented in this report, that the primary reaction to effective sexual stimulation is one of marked vasocongestion. These vascular responses include engorgement of the breasts; generalized body flush-phenomenon; engorgement of the clitoris; the size increase and vivid color changes of the "sex-skin" (labia minora); vaginal lubrication phenomenon as a secondary development to a vasocongestive reaction throughout the entire vaginal barrel; vasodistention of the outer third of the vagina to create an orgasmic platform, and sexually stimulated color changes in all organs of primary or secondary sexual response.

Apparently the human female responds to effective sexual stimulation, and prepares to accept the male in a typical "mounting-reaction" in a manner essentially akin to the localized congestive reaction which accomplishes erection of the male penis. The neurologic controls of these vasocongestive reactions in the human female have not been investigated.

IN SUMMATION

The gross anatomic reactions of the primary and secondary organs of sexual response to effective automanipulative and coital technics have been presented in detail, and related to the human sexual response cycle. The sexual cycle has been arbitrarily divided into four phases as the result of experience gained from 10 years of investigative effort. The stages of sexual response are in order: (1) Excitement Phase; (2) Plateau Phase; (3) Orgasm Phase; and (4) Resolution Phase.

The sexual response of increased breast vascularity, with resulting alteration in size, shape and anatomic configuration has been presented. Complete body distribution of the vascular flush phenomenon has also been detailed.

The descriptions of perineal reaction to sexual stimulation have included the labia majora effacement reaction, and the particular sex-response role and remarkable color alterations of the "sex-skin" (labia minora). In addition, the reactions of clitoris, urinary bladder, urethra and rectum to sexual tension have also been noted.

Multiple vaginal responses to effective sexual stimulation have been diagrammed and described in detail. These reactions include *Excitement Phase* development of the vaginal lubrication phenomenon, and the lengthening and distention of the inner two-thirds of the vagina; *Plateau Phase* vasocongestion of the outer one-third of the vagina with constriction of the central vaginal lumen; *Orgasmic Phase* contractions of this sex-tension platform created in the outer third of the vagina; and *Resolution Phase* involutional variations in anatomic structure.

The complete lack of cervical secretory function and the essentially negligible role of Bartholin gland secretory activity have also been pictured as a corollary to the description of the vaginal lubrication phenomenon.

It is apparent that the human female's somatic reaction to effective sexual stimulation is, primarily vasocongestive in nature. This response is centered in, but not completely confined to the organs of primary or secondary sexual response.

Acknowledgment. The technical assistance and complete cooperation of Mr. K. Cramer Lewis, Director of the Washington University Department of Medical Illustration, is gratefully acknowledged.

REFERENCES

1. BAUER, B. A. *Woman and love* (Trans. by Eden and Cedar Paul). New York: Boni & Liveright, 1927.
2. BEACH, F. A. *Hormones and behavior.* New York: Harper & Row, 1948.
3. BEACH, F. A. *Sexual behavior in animals and man.* Harvey Society Lectures (1947–1948) Series 43. Springfield, Illinois: Charles C Thomas, 1950.
4. BLOCH, I. *The sexual life of our time in its relations to modern civilization.* London: Rebman, 1908.
5. BROWN, F. R., and KEMPTON, R. T. *Sex questions and answers.* New York: McGraw-Hill, 1950.
6. DICKINSON, R. L., and BEAM, L. *A thousand marriages.* Baltimore: Williams & Wilkins, 1931.
7. DICKINSON, R. L. *Human sex anatomy* (ed. 2). Baltimore: Williams & Wilkins, 1933.
8. DICKINSON, R. L., and BEAM, L. *The single woman.* Baltimore: Williams & Wilkins, 1934.
9. ELLIS, H. *Studies in the psychology of sex.* New York: Random House, 1936.
10. FORD, C. S. *A comparative study of human reproduction.* New Haven, Connecticut: Yale University Press, 1945.
11. FORD, C. S., and BEACH, F. A. *Patterns of sexual behavior.* New York: Harper & Row, 1951.
12. GARDNER, W. U. Reproduction in the female. In J. F. Fulton (Ed.), *A textbook of physiology.* Philadelphia: W. B. Saunders, 1950 (Pp. 1162–1188).
13. GRAFENBERG, E. The role of the urethra in female orgasm. *Int. J. Sexol.,* 3, 145–148, 1950.
14. GRAY, H. (W. H. Lewis, Ed.) *Anatomy of the human body* (ed. 23). Philadelphia: Lea & Febiger, 1936.
15. HAIRE, N. *Encyclopedia of sexual knowledge.* New York: Eugenics Pub. Co., 1937.

16. HAIRE, N.　*Everyday sex problems*. London: Frederick Muller, 1948.

17. HARDENBERGH, E. W.　The psychology of feminine sex experience, *Int. J. Sexol.*, *2*, 224–228, 1949.

18. HIRSCHFELD, M.　*Folgen und Folgerungen*. Stuttgart: Julius Püttmann, 1928.

19. HORNSTEIN, F. X. von, and FALLER, A.　*Gesundes Geschlechtsleben*. Otten, Switzerland: Otto Walter, 1950.

20. HÜHNER, M.　*The diagnosis and treatment of sexual disorders in the male and female including sterility and impotence* (ed. 3). Philadelphia: F. A. Davis, 1945.

21. HUTTON, I. E.　*The sex technique in marriage* (Rev. ed.). New York: Emerson Books, 1942.

22. KAHN, F.　*Our sex life* (Trans. by G. Rosen). New York: Alfred A. Knopf, 1939.

23. KINSEY, A. C.　Sex behavior in the human animal. *Ann. New York Acad. Sci.*, *47*, 635–637, 1947.

24. KINSEY, A. C., POMEROY, W. B., and MARTIN, C. E.　*Sexual behavior in the human male*. Philadelphia: W. B. Saunders, 1948.

25. KINSEY, A. C., POMEROY, W. B., MARTIN, C. E., and GEBHARD, P.H.　Concepts of normality and abnormality in sexual behavior. In P. Hoch and J. Zubin (Eds.), *Psychosexual development in health and disease*. New York: Grune & Stratton, 1949 (Pp. 11–32).

26. KINSEY, A. C., POMEROY, W. B., MARTIN, C. E., and GEBHARD, P. H.　*Sexual behavior in the human female*. Philadelphia: W. B. Saunders, 1953.

27. KISCH, E. H.　*The sexual life of women in its physiological, pathological and hygienic aspects* (Orig. 1910, trans. by N. E. Paul). New York: Allied Book Co., 1926.

28. KRAFFT-EBING, R. VON　*Psychopathia sexualis, a medico-forensic study* (Trans. by F. J. Rebman). New York: Physicians & Surgeons Book Co., 1922.

29. MALCHOW, C. W.　*The sexual life*. St. Louis: C. V. Mosby, 1923.

30. MAXIMOV, A. A., and BLOOM, W.　*A text book of histology*. Philadelphia: W. B. Saunders, 1930.

31. MENDELSOHN, M.　Ist das Radfahren als eine gesundheitsgemässe Uebung anzusehen und aus ärztlichen Gesichtspunkten zu empfehlen? *Dtsch. med. Wchnschr.*, *22*, 381–384, 1896.

32. MOLL, A.　*The sexual life of the child*. New York: Macmillan, 1912.

33. MORAGLIA, G. B.　*Die Onanie beim normalen Weibe und bei den Prostituierten*. Berlin: Priber & Lammers, 1897.

34. NEGRI, V. *Psychoanalysis of sexual life*. Los Angeles: Western Institute of Psychoanalysis, 1949.
35. REICH, W. *The discovery of the orgone. Vol. 1: The function of the orgasm*. New York: Orgone Institute Press, 1942.
36. ROHLEDER, H. *Vorlesungen über Geschlechtstrieb und gesamtes Geschlechtsleben des Menschen*. Berlin: Fischers medicin. Buchhandlung, 1907.
37. ROUBAND, F. *Traite de l'impuissance et de la stérilité chez l'homme et chez la femme*. Paris: J. B. Baillière et Fils, 1876.
38. SADLER, W. S., and SADLER, LENA K. *Living a sane sex life*. Chicago: Wilcox & Follett, 1944.
39. SIEGLER, S. L. *Fertility in women*. Philadelphia: J. B. Lippincott, 1944.
40. SPALTEHOLZ, W. *Hand atlas of human anatomy* (Trans. by L. F. Barker) (ed. 7). Philadelphia: J. B. Lippincott, 1943.
41. STONE, HANNAH M., and STONE, A. *A marriage manual*. New York: Simon & Schuster, 1953.
42. TALMEY, B. S. *Neurasthenia sexualis*. New York: Practitioner's Publishing Co., 1912.
43. URBACH, K. Über die zeitliche Gefühlsdifferenz der Geschlechter während der Kohabitation. *Ztschr. f. Sexualwiss, 8,* 124–138, 1921.
44. VAN DE VELDE, T. H. *Ideal marriage*. New York: Covici Freide, 1930.
45. WEISMAN, A. I. *Spermatozoa and sterility*. New York: Harper & Row, 1941.
46. ZUCKERMAN, S. The menstrual cycle of the primates. *Proc. Zool. Soc.*, 1930, pp. 691–754.

4

THE SEXUAL RESPONSE
CYCLE OF THE
HUMAN FEMALE

2. The Clitoris: Anatomic and
Clinical Considerations *

The female phallus has stimulated an inexhaustible wellspring of sensate focus throughout recorded history. Theoretical definition of the role of the clitoris in female sexual response has created a literature that is a potpourri of behavioral concept unsupported by biologic fact. Obviously, centuries of "phallic fallacies" have done more to deter than to stimulate research interest in clitoral response to sexual stimulation.

Recently, investigative interests have centered on the anatomic and physiologic responses of the human male and female to sexual stimulation. The reactions of the female reproductive viscera (labial, vaginal, cervical and uterine responses) have been described in detail (24–29). Of the established pelvic reactions to sexual stimulation, the anatomic responses of the clitoris have been the most difficult to define, due to technical difficulties. For example, it is infinitely easier

* This investigation was supported in part by Research Grant RG-5998, Division of General Medical Sciences, Public Health Service, and in part by Ayerst Laboratories.

to detect finite variation in clitoral reaction during coition in the female superior or knee-chest positions than during the more routine female supine mountings. Obviously, with stimulative activity of either manual or mechanical origin, pudendal manipulation interferes with clinical observation.

Information to be presented is based on direct observation of over 300 women (ages 20 to 61) responding through complete orgasmic cycles in varied coital positionings and during autoerotic manipulation. Although investigative attention has not been focused constantly upon clitoral response, the information to be presented has been accrued primarily or secondarily from thousands of directly-observed cycles of female sexual response.

In addition to direct observation, simultaneous cinematography has recorded the gross anatomic reactions of the clitoris to sexual stimulation. Finite anatomic observation has been established by use of a colposcope (Zeiss, 6-40x magnification). One hundred selected female subjects have been observed over a 3-year period with the aid of modifications of basic colposcopic techniques. Clinical observations of clitoral and vaginal reaction during coital activity have been significantly clarified by the recent development of techniques of artificial coition (17).

Anatomic dissection, microscopic investigation and surgical ablation of the clitoris have established the organ as a homologue to the male penis (14, 32, 35). The clitoris consists of two corpora cavernosa enclosed in a dense membrane primarily of fibrous tissue origin, but also containing elastic fibers and smooth muscle bundles (6). The fibrous capsules unite along their medial surfaces to form a pectinoform septum which is well-interspersed with elastic and smooth muscle fibers. Each corpus is connected to the rami of the pubis and ischium by a crus. The clitoris is provided (like the penis) with a suspensory ligament which is inserted along the anterior surface of the midline septum. In addition, two small muscles, the ischiocavernosi, insert into the crura of the clitoris and have origin bilaterally from the ischial rami.

Anatomic dissection has been supplemented by clinical mensuration of the female phallus. Clitoral glans size has been reasonably established at an average of 4 to 5 mm. in both the transverse and the longitudinal (less accurate) axes. One hundred adult females were used in Dickinson's sample (8). He also described clitoral position with relation to the distance between the crural origins on the anterior border of the symphysis and the urethral meatus. A mean of 2.5 cm. was reported (9). In the literature, there are marked variations in reported clitoral length, but account frequently has not been taken of possible humoral source for the organ's obvious hypertrophy. It is obvious that descriptions of the exact origin of the clitoral crura on the anterior border of the symphysis or of the constant relation of crural origin to urethral meatus are an anatomic impossibility.

Aside from academic interest, Dickinson's focus in accumulating these data was to encourage clinical attempts to define clitoral function in female sexual response. In order to further his pioneer research interests, certain fundamental questions of clitoral reaction to sexual stimulation must be answered. (1) Are there consistent patterns of clitoral response within the framework of the four phases of the cycle of sexual response? (2) What anatomic changes occur in the clitoris during sexual stimulation? (3) Does the clitoris develop different response patterns during coition as opposed to reaction to manual or mechanical manipulation? (4) Are clitoral and vaginal orgasms truly separate *anatomic* entities? (5) What possible clinical application can be developed from the information accumulated to answer the four previous questions? These basic problems must be resolved before realistic concepts of the physiologic response of the clitoris to effective sexual stimulation can be established.

A discussion of the first two questions will be presented simultaneously in an attempt to define clitoral anatomic reaction to sexual stimulation, and to identify these response patterns within the loose clinical framework of the four phases of the female cycle of sexual response.

It should be reemphasized at the onset that there is normally marked variation in the anatomic structuring of the clitoris (Fig. 1, I). Clitoral glandes have been observed to measure only 2 to 3 mm. in transverse diameter. As opposed

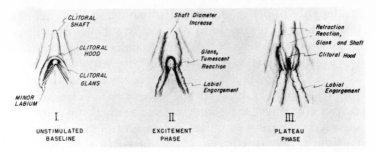

Figure 1. *Phase I: Unstimulated baseline.* The clitoral glans and shaft are illustrated in a sexually unstimulated state. The glans protrudes slightly from the minor labial clitoral hood. In many individuals the glans is completely covered by the hood. *Phase II: Excitement phase.* A twofold tumescent increase in glans diameter is illustrated. A clinically obvious tumescence of the clitoral glans occurs in less than half of sexually responding women. The increase in clitoral shaft diameter and engorgement of the minor labia are constant excitement phase responses to effective sexual stimulation. *Phase III: Plateau phase.* The retraction of the total clitoral body (glans and shaft) further broadens the shaft base as illustrated. There is no increase in glans diameter. The marked overhang of the clitoral hood is an anatomic indication of advanced sexual tension levels.

to this, a glans measuring a centimeter in transverse diameter is still within normal anatomic limits. There is also marked variation in crural and suspensory ligament origin from the lower to the upper border of the symphysis. The clitoral shaft (crura and corpora) may be quite long, thin and surmounted by a relatively small-sized glans, or short and thick with an enlarged glans. Frequently, the reverse of these combinations has been observed. Mensuration of shaft length has been so unreliable to date that results will not be reported.

The response patterns of the clitoris to effective sexual stimulation will be described in relation to the four phases of the cycle of sexual response. These phases (Excitement, Plateau, Orgasm, Resolution) have been established arbitrarily in an effort to clarify anatomic discussion (24).

The Excitement Phase. The first pelvic response to sexual stimulation of either psychic or physical origin is the production of vaginal lubrication (27). This material appears on the walls of the vaginal barrel within ten to thirty seconds from the onset of any form of sexually stimulative activity. Clitoral reaction does not develop as rapidly as the production of vaginal lubrication. Consequently, the widespread belief that the clitoris responds to sexual stimulation with a rapidity parallel to that of erection of the male penis is fallacious. The misconception that the clitoris reacts to sexual stimulation as quickly as the penis may have developed from the realization that the clitoris is a true anatomic homologue of the penis. The assumption that similar tissue structures would demonstrate parallel reactive abilities within a relatively equal time sequence is a natural error.

The reaction time of the clitoris to sexual stimulation also depends upon whether there is direct manipulation of the mons area, or whether sexually stimulative activity is focused upon other erotic areas of the female body. If only breast and/or vaginal manipulations occur (without direct clitoral contact), the clitoris develops the usual anatomic response patterns. However, there is a distinct delay in reaction time as opposed to the speed with which the clitoral response patterns develop subsequent to direct manipulation of the mons area.

During thousands of directly observed female sexual response cycles, more than half of the women provided no clinical evidence of a tumescent reaction of the clitoral glans. When clinical tumescence of the clitoral glans developed, the degree of vasocongestion ranged from a barely discernible increase to a two-fold expansion over the unstimulated diameter of the glans (Fig. 1, II). This reaction has been confused with penile erection and termed erection of the clitoris (15, 23). Clitoral erection has not been observed during this investigative program, unless there has been an obvious pathologic hypertrophy of the organ (30). As a general rule of thumb, the smaller the clitoral glans, the less frequently there is a clinically demonstrable tumescent reaction. However, some of the smaller organs have demonstrated the greatest relative size increase, while many of the larger clitorides have provided no gross evidence of a tumescent reaction.

Observable tumescence of the glans, when it occurs, does not develop until the individual sexual tensions have progressed well into the excitement phase of sexual response. The clitoris engorges in a response sequence that parallels that of vasocongestion of the minor labia. It may be recalled that the minor labia of the sexually responding human female increase in size to approximately twice their previous thickness, and provide external elongation for the internally expanding vaginal barrel (24, 26, 28). There is also a vasocongestive color change of the minor labia ("sex-skin") which includes the clitoral hood. However, these anatomic demonstrations of developing sexual tension do not occur until the degree of sexual stimulation has reached an advanced excitement phase. A similarly responding male has long since achieved full penile erection and, quite possibly, a moderate degree of elevation of at least one, if not both testicles (31).

Once observable tumescence of the clitoral glans develops, the reaction persists throughout the sexual response cycle, or for as long as an excitement phase degree of sexual stimulation is maintained.

There is no way of anticipating from observation in an unstimulated state whether a clitoral glans will develop a clinically obvious tumescence. However, when increase in size of the glans does occur the reaction pattern develops as a constant response to effective sexual stimulation. Variations in tumescent reactions of the glandes relate only to the degree and rapidity of size increase in response to direct manipulation as opposed to slower and less severe reaction patterns that develop during artificial coition or breast manipulation.

There is a clitoral response to sexual stimulation which occurs in every responding female during the excitement phase, regardless of whether there is clinically obvious tumescence of the glans. Under colposcopic examination, the superficial integument of the clitoral glans has been established as a movable membrane in a sexually unstimulated state. The superficial covering of the glans is wrinkled and moves without usual restriction over the underlying glans tissue exactly in the pattern of the integument of the unstimulated glans penis, but with less freedom than the skin of the scrotum. When any form of sexual tension develops, whether psychic or physical in origin, the clitoral glans always increases in size sufficiently to develop close apposition between underlying tissue and the loosely-applied, superficial integument. The vasocongestive reaction is of such finite nature that it usually cannot be noted by unsupported, clinical observation. This anatomic response to increasing sexual tension has been established with aid of the colposcope and its magnification (6-40x). This minimal degree of tumescence of the clitoral glans always develops with sexual tension, regardless of whether the vasocongestive process continues to a degree sufficient to establish a clinically observable tumescent reaction of the clitoral glans.

The shaft of the clitoris also undergoes an excitement phase vasocongestive reaction as the tissue structuring of the corpora cavernosa would suggest. There is definitive increase in shaft diameter which is a constant development regardless of corporal size. The vasocongestive increase in diameter of the clitoral shaft occurs at the same time that the observable tumescent reaction of the glans develops. However, the shaft increases in diameter whether or not the glans reacts to a clinically demonstrable degree.

Elongation of the clitoral shaft may occur in addition to the normal increase in shaft diameter. However, most clitorides go through the excitement-phase, vasocongestive period without developing clinically observable shaft elongation. Although objective observation is admittedly extremely difficult, an elongation response pattern has been firmly established in less than 10% of the observed orgasmic cycles. When clinical elongation of the shaft occurs, it does so without regard to source or type of sexual stimulation and as a reaction pattern that may not recur regularly with future sexual activity.

The Plateau Phase. The major clitoral response to effective sexual stimulation occurs in the plateau phase of the cycle of sexual response. This reaction develops with universal consistency. There is a retraction of the entire clitoral body and glans from its normal pudendal overhang position (Fig. 1, III). The crura of the clitoris and the suspensory ligament have major anatomic functions in this physiologic response. The ischiocavernosi apparently contribute actively to the retraction of the clitoris (as opposed to their function during male ejaculation). It should be emphasized that the exact roles of the crura, suspensory ligaments and muscle bundles have not been determined.

Regardless of the exact anatomic roles of the supportive tissues, this clitoral reaction to plateau phase levels of sexual response occurs in a constant pattern. The body and glans of the clitoris withdraw from normal pudendal overhang positioning and retract against the anterior border of the symphysis. Any portion of the clitoral glans that normally projects from the clitoral hood in a sexually unstimulated state withdraws deeply beneath the foreskin as the retraction reaction progresses. During the immediate preorgasmic sequence, the clitoris (shaft and glans) is extremely difficult to observe clinically. The retraction of the clitoral shaft is normally so marked that there is at least 50% over-all reduction in the length of the total clitoral body. The degree of the individual clitoral retraction reaction is best estimated under direct colposcopic observation.

During the plateau phase, the time sequence for glans and shaft retraction is subject to variation in relation to mode of sexual stimulation. During coition or breast manipulation, clitoral retraction develops late in the plateau phase as an indication of preorgasmic sex tension levels. With use of clitoral area manipulation, retraction of the clitoris frequently develops early in the plateau phase.

Obviously, the psychic components of the sexual response patterns cannot be equated objectively for each orgasmic cycle. However, it would be a major mistake to presume that psychic influence did not contribute to the reaction time of the individual female subject.

The retraction of the clitoris during the plateau phase is a reversible reaction. If high sexual tension levels are allowed to fall by deliberate withdrawal of stimulative techniques, the retracted body and glans will return to the normal pudendal overhang position. With return to effective sexual stimulation, clitoral retraction will recur. This reaction sequence may develop repetitively during long-maintained plateau phases when the individual female cannot quite obtain orgasmic release of sexual tensions.

It will be recalled that an observable tumescent increase in diameter develops constantly in the clitoral shaft but in less than 50% of the clitoral glandes during the excitement phase of sexual response. However, retraction of both the glans and shaft occurs as a constant reaction during the plateau phase regardless of whether the glans has developed an observable tumescent reaction.

Orgasmic Phase. No specific orgasmic phase reaction of the clitoris has been established.

Resolution Phase. After an orgasmic experience the return of the clitoris to normal pudendal overhang positioning occurs within 5 to 10 seconds after cessation of the vaginal "orgasmic platform" contractions. The plateau phase retraction of the clitoris is released as rapidly as detumescence of the "orgasmic platform" occurs, and as swiftly as the "sex skin" discoloration of the minor labia disappears (24). To provide further clinical concept of rapidity of occurrence, a parallel might be drawn to the male reaction pattern. The relaxation of the sexually retracted clitoral body with resultant elongation of the corpora cavernosa and the return of the glans to pudendal overhang positioning occurs roughly parallel in time sequence with the primary loss of the male erection after ejaculation (30).

When an observable tumescence of the glans has developed during the excitement phase, subsequent resolution phase detumescence is a relatively slow process. Particularly is this true for the individuals who demonstrate a two-fold vasocongestive increase in glans size. Although termination of the clitoral retraction reaction occurs very rapidly, continued clinical tumescence of the glans and vasocongestion of the shaft frequently have been observed to last five to ten minutes after orgasmic expression. Occasional women have demonstrated continued venous engorgement of the clitoris for fifteen to thirty minutes after an orgasmic phase experience.

Those individuals who achieve a plateau phase level of sexual response, but do not obtain orgasmic phase release of the accumulated sexual tensions occasionally maintain venous engorgement of the entire clitoris for a matter of hours after termination of all sexually stimulative activity.

In summation, the answers to the first two of the five questions that have directed the format of this report may be considered briefly. The anatomic changes that develop during sexual stimulation do so in a response pattern that may be consistently identified within the framework of the 4 phases of the cycle of sexual response. The exception to this statement is the fact that no specific reactions of the clitoris to an orgasmic phase experience have been identified.

The anatomic changes that develop in the clitoris during the cycle of sexual response are as follows.

Excitement Phase.

1. There is a constant tumescent reaction of the clitoral glans that is microscopic in character. Under supported observation (6-40x magnification) the wrinkled, loosely-applied, superficial integument of the clitoral glans is filled out by venous congestion of the underlying glans tissues.

2. Clinically obvious tumescence of the clitoral glans occurs in less than 50% of sexually stimulated women. When it does develop, it creates the impression of clitoral erection. No actual erection has been observed during this investigative program except in examples of pathologic clitoral hypertrophy.

3. A constant vasocongestive increase in the diameter of the clitoral shaft develops as sexual tensions mount.

4. There is a congestive elongation of the clitoral shaft which develops after the increase in diameter has been stabilized. However, the shaft elongation can be identified in less than 10% of sexually responding women.

Plateau Phase.
There is a constant retraction reaction of the combined clitoral glans and shaft that provides at least a 50% reduction in total clitoral length. This response to high levels of sexual tension elevates and effaces the clitoris along the anterior surface of the symphysis and retracts the entire clitoris deeply beneath the protective minor labial hood.

Resolution Phase. The retraction reaction of the clitoral glans and shaft is lost within a few seconds after female orgasmic experience. The tumescent reactions of the clitoral shaft and of the glans (when it occurs) take a matter of several minutes to resolve.

If orgasmic release of sexual tensions is not obtained, the clitoral retraction reaction is lost as rapidly as stimulative techniques are withdrawn, but clitoral tumescence of either glans or shaft may continue for a matter of hours after cessation of sexual activity.

With the clitoral anatomic reaction patterns established, there remain two questions of psychologic and physiologic import to discuss, and the possible clinical application of accumulated investigative material to consider.

Does the clitoris develop different response patterns during coition, as opposed to reaction to manual or mechanical manipulation?

Clitoral reactions were observed during coital activity in three positions: female supine, superior, and knee-chest and during both manual and mechanical manipulation. Investigations were conducted during natural coition in each position and with artificial coition in female supine and knee-chest positions. Clitoral response patterns were the most difficult to establish during female supine mountings. In this particular position, the technique of artificial coition provided the most objective information (17). In the female superior position, only natural coition could be accomplished satisfactorily. Regardless of coital positioning, or type of coition, the reactions of the clitoris to successful sexual stimulation followed the response patterns detailed in preceding portions of this report.

There were many instances of women failing to achieve orgasmic tension release, or of purposely being held at selected preorgasmic tension levels; so that long-maintained observation of clitoral reaction at both excitement and plateau phase levels of sexual response occurred frequently. Thus, multiple opportunities were provided for observation of the tumescent and retraction reactions of the clitoral glans and shaft without sudden termination of the experiments by orgasmic release of sexual tensions.

If clinically obvious tumescence of the glans occurred subsequent to mons manipulation, it also occurred with similar degrees of vasocongestion during coition in the three described positions. In reverse, no secondary clitoral tumescence developed during coition except that similar degrees of vasocongestion occurred also during primary clitoral area stimulation. When the mons area was manipulated directly, the observable tumescent reaction of the glans (if it developed) occurred earlier in the excitement phase than when the vasocongestive reaction developed during coital activity without direct clitoral area contact.

Tumescence of the clitoral shaft, which occurs in all women regardless of the presence or absence of an observable glans tumescence, also developed earlier in the excitement phase during primary mons manipulation as opposed to secondary coital stimulation.

Three women were able to achieve orgasmic response by breast manipulation alone, in addition to their ability to react successfully to mechanical or manual clitoral area manipulation and to natural or artificial coition. Observations of these women during breast manipulation recorded clitoral response patterns that were identical to those induced by mons manipulation or by natural or artificial coition. Only one of the three women demonstrated on observable, excitement phase tumescent reaction of the clitoral glans during breast-stimulated orgasmic response cycles. This secondary clitoral reaction developed late in the excitement phase paralleling clitoral response during artificial or natural coition. There was obvious delay in this secondary reaction when compared to response patterns developed during primary (mechanical or manual manipulation) of the clitoral area.

As anticipated, the retraction reaction of the clitoral glans and shaft developed during the plateau phase of sexual tension for all three women. The reaction sequence paralleled that achieved during intercourse (late plateau, preorgasmic phase), but was delayed as compared to the more rapid response patterns (early plateau phase) which occur during clitoral area manipulation.

Unfortunately, the women under investigation by the Reproductive Biology Research Foundation do not include individuals who can fantasy to orgasm. Therefore, observations of clitoral reaction patterns secondary to purely psychic sexual stimulation have been limited to excitement phase levels of sexual response. This level of sexual tension has been created frequently by exposing subjects to salacious literature. The clinical tumescent reaction of the clitoral glans could be demonstrated in only a few of the subjects who normally developed this reaction. When this vasocongestive reaction of the clitoris did occur, it developed long after there was obvious production of vaginal lubrication and paralleled a vasocongestive increase in the size of the minor labia. A minimum of one-half hour of exposure to pornographic literature was necessary to produce an observable tumescent reaction of the clitoral glans.

A microscopic vasocongestive reaction of the clitoral glans developed in approximately 75% of the women who were exposed to pornographic literature. It could be demonstrated shortly after vaginal lubrication was well-established. Fewer than one-third of the responding women produced a demonstrable increase in clitoral shaft diameter and no shaft elongation was observed.

The clitoris is quite unavailable to direct penile stimulation during either natural or artificial coition. The fact that the clitoris is not directly stimulated by intravaginal thrusting of the male penis does not preclude indirect stimulation during coition. Clitoral stimulation during coitus in the female supine position develops indirectly from distention of the minor labia at the vaginal vestibule by the penile shaft. A mechanical traction develops on both sides of the clitoral hood subsequent to penile distention of the vaginal outlet. With penile thrust, the entire clitoral body is pulled toward the pudendum by traction exerted on the wings of the minor labial hood.

When the penile shaft is withdrawn during active coition, traction on the clitoral hood is somewhat relieved and the body and glans return to the normal pudendal overhang positioning. Coital traction of the clitoris toward the vaginal outlet does not develop sufficient organ excursion to allow direct penile/clitoral contact. This rhythmic movement of the clitoral body in conjunction with intravaginal thrusting and withdrawal of the penis develops significant secondary sexual tension levels.

It should be emphasized that this same type of secondary clitoral stimulation occurs in every coital position, when there is a full penetration of the vaginal barrel by the erect penis. Anatomic exceptions to this statement are created by any significant artificial (parity) gaping of the vaginal outlet.

It is also obvious that there is a psychic component of active coition which contributes to secondary clitoral stimulation. This occurs regardless of coital positioning as sexual tensions increase. It is impossible to assign a discrete anatomic role to this type of secondary clitoral influence. It will remain for more sophisticated methods of neurophysiologic and psychiatric investigation to assign individual roles to the multiple influences, which create the total picture of secondary clitoral stimulation.

The female superior coital position allows direct propioceptive stimulation of the clitoris with male pelvic thrust. In this coital position the clitoris may be stimulated directly by the close apposition of the male and female symphyses. There also remains the constant secondary stimulation of clitoral hood traction during active coition.

In the knee-chest position, no direct stimulation on the clitoris is possible. Yet, the clitoris undergoes normal anatomic response patterns as female sexual tensions increase. Observable clitoral tumescence, when it occurs during the excitement phase, and clitoral retraction, which is a constant factor in the plateau phase, occur in the vasocongestive response patterns established for the individual female. In this coital position, clitoral stimulation develops as a secondary response to clitoral hood traction and, of course, as a secondary behavioral response to the developing tensions of active coition.

There have been no variations in clitoral response patterns (other than increased rapidity of reaction) during hundreds of orgasmic cycles produced by mechanical or manual manipulation of the clitoral area, as opposed to the response

patterns which develop during successful (orgasmic achievement) coition in any of the three described coital positions.

*Are clitoral and vaginal orgasms truly separate ana-
tomic entities?*

The analytical literature abounds with descriptions and
discussions of vaginal as opposed to clitoral orgasms (3, 5, 7,
12, 13, 16, 20, 21). From an *anatomic* point of view, there is
absolutely no difference in the responses of the pelvic viscera
to effective sexual stimulation, regardless of whether the stimulation occurs as a result of clitoral area manipulation, natural
or artificial coition, or, for that matter, breast manipulation
alone.

With the technique of artificial coition, the reactions
of the vagina during coition have been directly observed and
repetitively recorded through the medium of cinematography.
These reactions were first observed during sexual response
cycles stimulated by clitoral area manipulation (24–26). During
artificial coition, the reactions of the vaginal barrel conformed
in exact detail to the vaginal response patterns which developed subsequent to mons manipulation.

It should be stated parenthetically that these same intravaginal reaction patterns were developed by the three women
who are capable of achieving orgasmic response to breast
stimulation alone. These individuals also developed identical
vaginal barrel response patterns with clitoral area manipulation and during artificial coition. In other words, from an
anatomic point of view, complete sexual response cycles,
whether induced by clitoral area, vaginal or breast stimulation, provide identical pelvic reaction patterns. The human
female's physiologic responses to effective sexual stimulation
develop with consistency regardless of the source of the psychic
or somatic sexual stimulation.

Clinical Application of Research Information. The
literature abounds with discussions of the role of the clitoris
in female sexual response. There is essential accord in the view
that the primary function of the organ is to stimulate female
sexual tension. There is little agreement on the specific roles

clitoral anatomy and physiology play in influencing female psychosexual response.

Both the size of the clitoral glans and its positioning on the anterior border of the symphysis have been considered of major importance in female response to sexual stimulation (1, 8–10, 18, 33, 37, 38). These two problems will be considered in order. Observation of thousands of sexual response cycles has confirmed Dickinson's conviction (8, 9) that there is no relation between the size of the clitoris and its influence on female sexual response. The anatomic responses to excitement and plateau phase levels of sexual tension develop without relation to the unstimulated size of the clitoris. For example, two sexually mature women may be observed through entire sexual response cycles. One woman may have an unstimulated clitoral glans measuring 3 mm. in diameter and the other a glans that is 1 cm. in diameter. Both women may respond to sexual stimulation with a tumescent increase in diameter of the glandes. Two different women with similar unstimulated diameter of the glans clitoris may not develop observable tumescent reaction during excitement phases of successful sexual response cycles. Regardless of the size of the unstimulated glans or the occurrence of a specific, observable tumescent reaction, the four sexually mature women may reach orgasmic phase levels of sexual response with equal facility presuming the sources of sexual stimulation are reasonably standardized.

Dickinson (9) originally emphasized the fact that women with histories of decades of regular masturbatory activity do not develop a consistent hypertrophy of the clitoris. There is no longer doubt that severe, long-maintained masturbatory patterns occasionally produce measurable increases in the unstimulated diameter of the clitoral glans (30). The individuals who develop this secondary hypertrophy are usually those who employ mechanical methods for clitoral stimulation. They are few in number, and represent only minor exceptions to the general rule that clitoral hypertrophy does not result from masturbatory activity.

In conjunction with the discussion of clitoral size in relation to sexual response must go consideration of clitoral positioning in relation to female sexuality. The theoretical importance of both factors has been dealt with at length in the literature (1, 8–10, 18, 33, 37, 38). Clitoral position on the anterior border of the symphysis has been considered of real importance in the facility of female sexual response during coition. The anatomic background for clitoral stimulation during active coition has been considered in the foregoing. In essence, the clitoral stimulation which occurs during active coition is the secondary result of traction on the minor labial hood which develops subsequent to penile distention of the vaginal vestibule. Labial hood traction occurs regardless of where the clitoral crura have origin on the pubic rami, and is just as severe for high as for low origin sites.

There is a fallacious concept that a low implantation of the clitoris on the anterior border of the symphysis tends to improve the sexuality of the individual female due to increased possibility of direct penile contact. In spite of low clitoral positioning, the penis rarely comes in contact with the clitoris during active coition. This observation has been established with the aid of the recently developed technique of artificial intercourse. In addition, the clitoral-body retraction which always develops during the plateau phase further removes the clitoral glans from the theoretical possibility of direct penile contact.

The importance of developing specific coital techniques for clitoral stimulation has in the past been repetitively emphasized (18, 19, 22, 34, 36–38). Unless the male partner makes a specific effort to ride high over the female pelvis in the female supine position and to bring the shaft of the penis in direct apposition to the total mons area, the clitoris is not directly stimulated by penile thrust. This coital position is difficult to maintain with consistency during increasing sexual tension, particularly if the female does not have parous relaxation of the vaginal outlet. The nulliparous female may not be able to retain a penis in this position without personal discomfort developing at the vaginal outlet. If successful penile positioning is maintained, the female partner may complain of distressing rectal pressure with the active thrusting of a penis held high over the perineum and directed toward the terminal bowel by a tight fourchette.

The necessity for primary stimulation of the clitoral

glans by the penile shaft is purely theoretical, created by our phallic-fallacy literature. It does not take into account the secondary clitoral stimulation that develops subsequent to hood traction, or the psychosexual stimulation that develops during active coition. The stimulative strength that both of these factors represent has been repetitively manifested in observable reaction patterns of the clitoral body and glans during the various phases of the sexual response cycle.

The techniques of and reactions to direct clitoral manipulation should be discussed in detail. Observations of foreplay response patterns in higher animals first sensitized investigators to the clinical importance of effective stimulative techniques (2, 11). Marriage manuals discuss at length the importance of clitoral manipulation as the basis of adequate coital foreplay. Discussions of female sexual response have focused on the questions of why and when to stimulate the clitoris. To date, little has been said in the infinitely more important direction of how to manipulate the clitoris, and how much stimulation is usually required. Direct observation of both mechanical and manual manipulative activity through repetitive orgasmic response cycles in over 300 women has emphasized the fundamental importance of the questions of "how?" and "how much?". No two individual women were observed to proceed identically. Yet, while there are innumerable variations in manipulative technique, all of the women had one inclination in common.

It is a rare woman who directly manipulates the clitoris, or, if she does, maintains this type of stimulative activity for any significant length of time. Seldom does the responding female directly manipulate the clitoris through an entire sexual response cycle. In most instances, manual application is applied to the general mons area, either to the right or left side of the clitoral shaft, depending entirely on whether the individual is right or left handed. As a general rule direct clitoral-body stimulation is less effective in developing and/or maintaining sexual tension than is indirect stimulation developed through manipulation of the entire mons area. The clitoral response patterns occur just as effectively, if the mons area is stimulated, if the clitoral hood is pulled by manual traction (simulating coital activity), or, if the breasts alone are manually stimulated.

Immediately after orgasm, the clitoral glans is an extremely sensitive organ for most sexually responding women. While there is no demonstrable physical change of the glans during orgasmic expression, a significant degree of hypersensitivity does develop at the peak of the sexual response cycle. Most women prefer that the clitoral glans not be directly manipulated at high plateau, during orgasm or early in resolution phase levels of the sexual response cycle.

Evidence of the extreme tactile sensitivity of the entire mons area as opposed to the clitoris alone has been presented by the Kinsey Institute for Sex Research (18). During the gynecologic phase of their investigation, the minor labia were determined to be almost as perceptive to finite tactile sensation as the clitoris. The Institute also considers the minor labia to be fully as important as the clitoris as a source of erotic arousal. Additional suggestion of mons area sensitivity is provided by the observation that after clitoridectomy, masturbation has been conducted as effectively as prior to surgery by manipulation of the mons area alone (4).

The present authors' research program has supported another clinical observation. Most women prefer continual manipulation of the clitoral area during the entire orgasmic phase of the sexual response cycle. This parallels their observed interest in continuing active coital movement (pelvic thrust) during an orgasmic experience developing during active coition. The desire for continued stimulative activity during actual orgasmic expression is in opposition to the average male approach to orgasmic response during coition. Most males attempt the deepest possible vaginal penetration, as the orgasmic phase develops, and maintain this enveloped vaginal position during ejaculation, rather than continue the rapid, pelvic thrusting of preorgasmic sexual tension (30).

It should also be noted that the sexually mature female is usually not content with one orgasmic experience during episodes of clitoral manipulation. Most women prefer a minimum of two or three orgasmic expressions before they reach satiation, if there is not unusual psychosocial detraction from their basic sexual tension levels. In many instances, actively masturbating women controlling their own sexual response levels will experience five to twenty recurrent orgasmic experiences with sexual tension never allowed to drop below a plateau phase maintenance level until physical exhaustion terminates the session.

An anatomic pattern of clitoral response has created confusion for the male partner as evidenced in guidelines hopefully created by the inexhaustible marriage-manual literature. This is the retraction reaction of the clitoral glans and shaft which elevates the organ high on the anterior border of the symphysis, away from its normal pudendal overhang position, during the plateau and orgasmic phases of female sexual response. This anatomic evidence of high levels of female sexual tension creates a problem for the uninitiated male. If the suggestions of the marriage manuals are followed, the male develops the concept that he is to find the clitoris and stay with it. In the first place, the concept of manipulating only the clitoris rather than the entire mons area is grossly in error, as has been discussed. In the second place, it is technically difficult for the male partner to stay with the clitoris, when it retracts high onto the anterior border of the symphysis, well away from its previous pudendal overhang position. Clitoral-body retraction causes many a male to lose contact with the organ. Having lost contact, the male partner frequently ceases active manipulation of the general mons area and attempts to locate the clitoris. In this manner, a marked state of sexual frustration is produced for the female partner. By the time the clitoral shaft has been relocated, the plateau level of female sexual response frequently has been lost.

It is important to emphasize the fact that the retracted shaft of the clitoris continues to be stimulated through traction on the protective clitoral hood and manipulation of the general mons area. The proprioceptive stimulus developed by the clitoral hood traction is more effective than direct manipulation of the clitoris, particularly if any untoward pressure is applied to the clitoral body or glans.

SUMMARY

In brief summary it may be stated that the clitoris develops identical response patterns regardless of whether the source of sexual stimulation is active coition or manual or mechanical manipulation.

Clitoral and vaginal orgasms are identical *anatomic* entities from the viewpoint of female pelvic reaction to successful sexual stimulation.

Direct stimulation of the clitoris is rarely accomplished during intercourse other than in the female superior position. The secondary influences of traction on the clitoral hood by penile distention of the vaginal vestibule and the psychosexual influences of active coition are all that are necessary to initiate a complete clitoral response pattern regardless of the coital positioning.

Direct stimulation of the clitoris is rarely desired or effected by women during self-applied activity. In most instances, manipulation of the mons area with resultant secondary stimulation of the shaft and glans is the technique of choice and reproduces in exact detail the clitoral anatomic reaction patterns which develop during active coition.

REFERENCES

1. BAUER, B. A.   *Woman and love* (Trans. by Eden and Cedar Paul). New York: Boni & Liveright, 1927.
2. BEACH, F. A.   A review of physiological and psychological studies of sexual behavior in mammals. *Physiol. Rev.*, 27, 240–307, 1947.
3. BEAUVOIR, SIMONE DE   *The second sex* (Trans. by H. M. Parshley). New York: Alfred A. Knopf, 1952.
4. BONAPARTE, MARIE   Notes sur l'excision clitoridectomie. *R. Française de Psychanalyse, 12,* 213–231, 1948.
5. CHIDECKEL, M.   *Female sex perversion.* New York: Eugenics Pub. Co., 1935.
6. DANESINO, V., and MARTELLA, E.   Modern concepts of the function of the corpora cavernosa of the vagina and clitoris. *Arch. di Obstet. e Ginec., 60,* 150–167, 1956.
7. DEUTSCH, HELENE   *The psychology of women.* New York: Grune & Stratton, 1945 (Vol. 2, p. 80).
8. DICKINSON, R. L., and PIERSON, H. H.   The average sex life of American women. *J.A.M.A., 85,* 1113–1117, 1925.

9. DICKINSON, R. L. *Atlas of human sex anatomy* (ed. 2). Baltimore: Williams & Wilkins, 1949.
10. ELLIS, H. *Studies in the psychology of sex.* New York: Random House, 1936.
11. FORD, C. S., and BEACH, F. A. *Patterns of sexual behavior.* New York: Harper & Row, 1951.
12. FREUD, S. *New introductory lectures on psychoanalysis* (Trans. by W. J. H. Sprott). New York: W. W. Norton, 1933.
13. FREUD, S. *A general introduction to psychoanalysis* (Trans. by J. Riviere). New York: Perma Giants, 1935.
14. GRAY, J. (W. H. Lewis, Ed.). *Anatomy of the human body* (ed. 23). Philadelphia: Lea & Febiger, 1936.
15. GUZE, H. Anatomy and physiology of sex. In A. Ellis and A. Abarbanel (Eds.), *Encyclopedia of sexual behavior.* New York: Hawthorn Books, 1961 (Vol. 1, pp. 110–118).
16. HITSCHMANN, E., and BERGLER, E. *Frigidity in women, its characteristics and treatment* (Trans. by P. L. Weil). Washington and New York: Nervous and Mental Disease Pub. Co., 1936.
17. JOHNSON, VIRGINIA E., and MASTERS, W. H. The physiology of intravaginal contraceptive failure. *West. J. Surg., Obst. & Gynec., 70,* 202–207, 1962.
18. KINSEY, A. C., POMEROY, W. B., MARTIN, C. F., and GEBHARD, P. H. *Sexual behavior in the human female.* Philadelphia: W. B. Saunders, 1953.
19. KLEEGMAN, SOPHIE J. Frigidity in women. *Quart. Rev. Surg., Obst. & Gynec., 16,* 243–248, 1959.
20. KNIGHT, R. P. Functional disorders in the sexual life of women. *Bull. Menninger Clin., 7,* 25–35, 1943.
21. KROGER, W. S., and FREED, S. C. Psychosomatic aspects of frigidity. *J.A.M.A., 143,* 526–532, 1950.
22. LANDIS, C., and BOLLES, M. M. *Personality and sexuality of physically handicapped women.* New York: Harper & Row, 1942.
23. MASSERMAN, J. H. *Principles of dynamic psychiatry.* Philadelphia: W. B. Saunders, 1946.
24. MASTERS, W. H. The sexual response cycle of the human female: I. Gross anatomic considerations. *West. J. Surg., Obst. & Gynec., 68,* 57–72, 1960.
25. MASTERS, W. H., and JOHNSON, VIRGINIA E. The human female: Anatomy of sexual response. *Minnesota Med., 43,* 31–36, 1960.
26. MASTERS, W. H., and JOHNSON, VIRGINIA E. Orgasm, anatomy of the female. In A. Ellis and A. Abarbanel (Eds.), *Encyclopedia of sexual behavior.* New York: Hawthorn Books, 1961 (Vol. 2, pp. 788–793).

27. MASTERS, W. H.   The sexual response cycle of the human female: II. Vaginal lubrication. *Ann. New York Acad. Sci. 83*, 301-317, 1959.

28. MASTERS, W. H., and JOHNSON, VIRGINIA E.   The physiology of the vaginal reproductive function. *West. J. Surg., Obst. & Gynec., 69*, 105–120, 1961.

29. MASTERS, W. H., and JOHNSON, VIRGINIA E.   The artificial vagina: Anatomic, physiological, psychosexual function. *West. J. Surg., Obst. & Gynec., 69*, 192–212, 1961.

30. MASTERS, W. H., and JOHNSON, VIRGINIA, E.   Unpublished data.

31. MASTERS, W. H., and JOHNSON, VIRGINIA E.   The anatomy and physiology of human sexual response. In C. W. Lloyd (Ed.), *Human reproduction and sexual behavior.* Philadelphia: Lea & Febiger, 1964.

32. REYNOLDS, S. R. M.   *Physiological basis of gynecology and obstetrics.* Springfield, Illinois: Charles C Thomas, 1959.

33. ROHLEDER, H.   *Vorlesungen über Geschlechstrieb und gesamtes Geschlechtsleben des Menschen.* Berlin: Fischers medicin. Buchhandlung, 1907.

34. SADLER, W. S., and SADLER, LENA K.   *Living a sane sex life.* Chicago: Wilcox & Follett, 1944.

35. SPALTEHOLZ, W.   *Hand atlas of human anatomy* (Trans. by L. F. Barker) (ed. 7). Philadelphia: J. B. Lippincott, 1943 (Vol. 3).

36. STONE, HANNAH M., and STONE, A.   *A marriage manual.* New York: Simon & Schuster, 1953.

37. VAN DE VELDE, T. H.   *Ideal marriage.* New York: Covici Freide, 1930.

38. WRIGHT, H.   *Sex factor in marriage.* London: Williams & Norgate, 1930.

5

EXPERIMENTAL STUDIES OF MATING BEHAVIOR IN ANIMALS

Sex research has a long history, but during the past few decades there have been several important and exciting advances. In part this is due to a marked increase in the number of scientists investigating problems of sexual behavior. Techniques have become more rigorous and sophisticated, and new theoretical formulations have been developed.

SEXUAL BEHAVIOR AND EVOLUTION

From the broad point of view, some of the most penetrating and fundamental questions that can be asked about sexual behavior have to do with its relationships to evolution. These problems do not concern psychologists in their day-to-day work, but they are problems that should not be forgotten.

Two questions are very important to many biologically oriented scientists. (1) How have evolutionary changes affected sexual behavior? (2) How has sexual behavior affected the course of evolution? As introductory reading for anyone interested in these questions, I recommend a book entitled *Behavior and Evolution* by Roe and Simpson (1958).

One way in which sexual behavior can influence the course of evolution is reflected in the concept of isolating mechanisms.

Evolution implies change. It demands the emergence of new species, but at the same time it demands a high degree of stability and integrity of existing groups. If different kinds of animals were to interbreed and freely produce large numbers of viable and fertile hybrid offspring, the original genotypes could eventually be submerged and lost. This does not, in fact, occur. Two species may be prevented from interbreeding by one or a combination of types of barriers or isolating mechanisms that have been classified by Dobzhansky (1941) and by Mayr (1942). These may be geographical, as when two species are separated by a body of water or a mountain range. They may be temporal, when the species live together but breed at different times of the year. Isolating mechanisms may also be behavioral or psychological. For example, it is sometimes possible to discover two sympatric species that can produce viable and fertile hybrids in artificial conditions but never do so in nature. Some instances of so-called psychological isolation present problems that are very familiar to the experimental psychologist. These may include species differences in sensory capacity, in perceptual organization, in motivational patterns, or even in early life experience, which contribute to the prevention of sexual mixture with the production of fertile hybrids which could successfully compete with the parental stocks.

In some instances, males and females of different species never attempt copulation although there seems to be some initial attraction. This can occur because one element in the premating courtship of one species is lacking in that of the other.

When a male Siamese fighting fish (*Betta splendens*) is ready to mate, he builds a bubble nest on the top of the water. When a female swims by, he executes certain courtship movements, the female approaches, and mating occurs under the bubble nest (Fig. 1). There are closely related species of fish

Figure 1. Mating embrace of the Siamese fighting fish, *Betta splendens;*
male wrapped around female beneath bubble nest

in which the male does not build the bubble nest, although the
courtship pattern is much the same as that of *Betta splendens.*
A female *Betta* may initially respond to the courtship invita-
tions of a male from the non-nestbuilding species, but in the
absence of a nest she soon loses interest and departs before the
mating can be consummated.

Male frogs and toads of many species form breeding
choruses that function to attract gravid females. Field and
laboratory studies have shown that at least for some species
females are attracted to and stimulated by calls of males of
their own kind but do not react to the masculine vocalizations
of a different species (Blair, 1956).

Some male birds announce their establishment of a breeding territory with a courtship song unique to their own species. New methods of recording and analyzing these songs have thrown light upon the role of vocal signals in sexual courtship as it relates to the evolutionary process. Figure 2 illustrates such recordings which are called sonograms or sound spectrographs. The ordinate shows the frequency, and time is represented along the abscissa. These are songs of the chiffchaff, willow warbler, and wood warbler. They are quite distinct to the human ear, but the chiffchaff and willow warbler

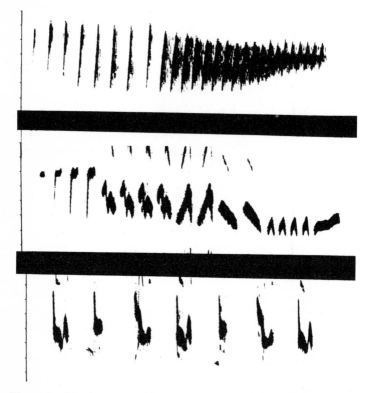

Figure 2.   Sound spectrographs of the songs of three western European birds: Top line, the chiffchaff (*Phylloscopus collybita*); second line, the willow warbler (*P. trochilus*); third line, the wood warbler (*P. sibilatrix*)

are so similar in appearance that an experienced ornithologist has to take them carefully in hand and examine them very closely to determine whether they belong to the same or different species. As long ago as 1789, the famous English naturalist, Gilbert White, observed that he could easily discriminate these species in the field simply by listening to their songs. What I want to point out here is that now the differences are apparent to anyone when new methods of recording the behavior are employed. Furthermore, this method yields records that can be dealt with on a quantitative basis.

Not only are there differences in the songs of different species, but within the same species there may be local dialects. For example, near the University of California white crown sparrows sing a Berkeley dialect, whereas white crown sparrows living three miles away sing a different dialect. Marler and his students have shown that dialects are learned by young birds during the fledgling period several months before they are capable of song production (Marler and Tamura, 1962).

It is conceivable that minor differences in the courtship song have an effect upon the choice of a mate. If this were true, local dialect differences might constitute a mechanism whereby new species start to emerge.

There have been several studies of isolating mechanisms in mammals, including the European vole (Godfrey, 1958) and various species of deer mice, *Peromyscus* (Eisenberg, 1962). We are working with several species of these mice in my laboratory. They apparently do not interbreed, and we would like to find out why. Mr. Lyn Clemens is studying their mating patterns to see if some fundamental differences are present. We would like also to find out whether or not males or females of one kind are attracted to females of another species and vice versa. To answer this question Clemens has just begun to study what might be called "choice of neighbors."

The experimental situation permits a mouse to spend his time next door to an unoccupied compartment previously inhabited by an individual of his own species, a different compartment which previously housed a mouse of a foreign species, or a compartment in which no mice have been kept. Alternatively the stimulus compartments may contain mice of one or another species. Very preliminary observations on very few animals suggest that males of two species show little or no selectivity as far as their choice of neighbors is concerned. They may spend equal amounts of time in the vicinity of a female of their own kind and one of another species. In contrast some females do seem to exhibit discriminatory behavior over a period of twenty-four hours. A given female may spend twice as much time in a compartment that previously contained a male of her own type that she devotes to the exploration and occupation of a chamber that previously housed a male of a different species. We suspect that the discrimination is made on the basis of olfactory cues, but we are not sure and it will be necessary to test this hypothesis.

Thus far the discussion has dealt with the problem of how established species may be prevented from interbreeding. A different question deals with the ways in which species differences in sexual behavior may have evolved. It should be noted parenthetically that when biologists and psychologists ask apparently similar questions about behavior, they may be looking for quite dissimilar answers. For example, when a psychologist asks why an animal exhibits a particular type of behavior he is usually concerned with problems of motivation; whereas, when a zoologist asks the same question, he means how did the behavior "get that way," that is, what were the evolutionary origins? Important studies dealing with the second question have involved attempts to duplicate certain aspects of evolutionary change under controlled conditions. This has sometimes involved the use of controlled breeding techniques combined with careful study of behavior in successive generations.

HEREDITY AND SEXUAL BEHAVIOR

An outstanding example of this approach is represented by the work of Stella Crossley (Pearce, 1960) on two mutant types of the fruit fly, Drosophila. One mutant, known as Ebony, is a dark color. The other, called Vestigial, possesses very short, stubby wings that are inadequate for flight.

In 1956 Knight, Robertson, and Waddington allowed Ebony and Vestigial flies to interbreed for eighteen successive generations. The number of hybrid offspring progressively decreased and eventually dropped to zero. To determine why this occurred, Crossley repeated the original experiment with two important modifications. First she made direct observations of the sexual behavior. Second, in each generation, she eliminated the offspring that resulted from cross-mating between Ebony and Vestigial parents.

In the first generation, Ebony females mated equally with Ebony or Vestigial males. In contrast, from the very beginning, Vestigial females showed a measurable though not exclusive preference for mating with males of their own type. Direct observation of individual matings revealed that selective breeding over forty generations produced two progressive changes. (1) Both Ebony and Vestigial females showed an increase in the frequency and vigor of certain stereotyped movements which they used to repel the courting male. Since these movements were employed to reject males of the opposite type, they reduced the frequency of heterospecific matings. (2) At the same time, as the number of inbred generations increased, males became increasingly responsive to the females' repelling movements and tended to break off their initial attempts at courtship after shorter periods. The combined result was that no hybrid offspring were produced after forty generations.

Now, if we make the assumption that in their natural environment the offspring of heterospecific matings would be inferior in the capacity for survival or in reproductive potential, then Crossley's experiment can be taken as a model for the kind of changes which could conceivably lead to the emergence of two incipient species. It is important to stress the fact that these changes involve only behavior.

Other isolating mechanisms exist, of course, and the natural situation is much more complex than any laboratory experiment could reveal. Nonetheless, this particular study serves as an example of the way in which experimental methods can be applied to problems of behavioral evolution. At the same time it calls attention to the importance of genetical factors influencing sexual behavior.

There are two obvious ways of investigating the relationship between heredity and behavior. One is to begin with two populations which are known to have different genotypes and to examine them for behavioral differences. The second approach, often employed in conjunction with the first, and exemplified by the work of Crossley described above, involves selective breeding of successive generations to produce individuals of the desired behavioral phenotype.

During the past decade many psychologists have used the first method to show that inbred strains of mice differ from one another in terms of general activity, learning, aggressiveness, emotionality, and even in the preference for ethyl alcohol over branch water (McClearn and Rodgers, 1961). Years ago, Robert Tryon employed selective breeding to create strains of maze-bright and maze-dull rats (Tryon, 1929).

The literature includes very few relevant reports dealing with sexual behavior, and in this connection it is important to stress the fact that the most elaborate and detailed information concerning genotypical differences is valueless unless it is coupled with equally precise and reliable measures for behavior. Behavioral endpoints must be as objectively and quantitatively defined as are the genetical variables.

These desiderata have been approached within reasonable limits in few published studies. W. C. Young and his coworkers have measured the sexual behavior of three strains or families of guinea pigs. Two strains have been inbred for approximately eighty generations and the third is a heterogeneous strain, maintained without any attempt at genetic selection. Carefully devised measures of "sex drive" were applied to males of these three strains. It was found that the within-strain variance was small for inbred types and quite marked for the heterogeneous strain. In addition, "sex drive" was low for males of inbred strains as compared with males of the third strain, which had never been inbred (Valenstein, Riss and Young, 1955).

At the University of California in Berkeley, we maintain two strains of rats that are descendants of those bred by Tryon in his work on the inheritance of maze-learning ability. These strains, now known as S_1 and S_3, are the subject of intensive study on the differences in the biochemistry of various brain regions. Differences have been found in enzyme activity that correlate with differences in learning ability (Rosenzweig, Krech, and Bennet, 1960).

Working at Berkeley while on leave from Yale, R. Whalen (1961) conducted standardized sex tests on male rats from the S_1 and S_3 strains. He found that although they were closely similar in many respects, males from the two strains differed significantly in terms of certain standard measures of sexual behavior.

One of our most reliable indices to sexual activity in the male rat is the number of intromissions that precede the occurrence of ejaculation or orgasm. Whalen found that the S_3 males reached the threshold for ejaculation after fewer intromissions than were required by members of the S_1 strain. This is of more than incidental interest because the frequency of intromissions seems to influence the probability of successful pregnancy in this species.

Studies such as those of Young and of Whalen automatically lead to more detailed investigations. For example, one of the first questions that Dr. Young asked after discovering strain differences in the sex drive of guinea pigs was whether this could be due to differences in the output of androgen by the testes. Subsequent experiments showed that this was not the case. One cannot eradicate the strain difference by simply giving the strain that is low on sex drive large amounts of male hormone (Grunt and Young, 1952).

Whalen's experiments with the S_1 and S_3 males reminded me of earlier studies by McGaugh, who investigated maze learning in the same strains. He found that although S_3 rats tend to be inferior, they can be brought up to the performance level of S_1 animals if they are given diazadamantan— a drug which acts as a cerebral excitant. Under the influence of this drug S_3 rats do as well in a maze as the S_1 animals (McGaugh, Westbrook, and Burt, 1961). Preliminary experiments on mating behavior suggest that strain differences are temporarily eliminated by the same pharmacological agent. This work must be repeated with added controls and a larger N, but the problem seems worthy of investigation.

The technique of selective breeding has rarely been

used in the study of sexual behavior. A number of years ago, Wulf Rasmussen, at the University of Oslo, published a preliminary report to the effect that the level of sex drive in mice and rats can be altered by selective breeding (Rasmussen, 1953). A more recent and promising program along these same lines is being carried out by Dr. Thomas McGill at Williams College. To date, McGill has published several very important findings (McGill and Blight, 1963). The first is that standardized measures of sexual performance reveal reliable differences between some inbred strains of mice. A second contribution has resulted from crossing certain strains and testing the sexual behavior of the F_1 hybrids. Table 1 shows

TABLE 1   MEDIAN SCORES FOR MALE MICE OF THREE STRAINS AND SIGNIFICANCE LEVELS OF THE THREE POSSIBLE COMPARISONS FOR EACH MEASURE

Measure	Median scores [a]			Significance levels (Two-tailed)		
	C57/ BL/6J	DBA/ 2J	BDF_1 [b]	C57 vDBA	C57 $vBDF_1$	DBA $vBDF_1$
1. ML	42	85	42	.02		.002
2. TNT	400	129	546	.002		.002
3. No. of I.	17	5	18	.02		.02
4. % Bite	0	20	0	.02		.001
5. ED	23	17	19	.02	.02	
6. T of I	15	20	19	.02	.01	
7. No. HM	2	0.5	0	.01	.001	
8. III	28	137	42	.002	.002	.002
9. T of M	2	7	3	.002	.001	.02
10. PIMD	1	4	2	.002	.02	.002
11. No. of M	18	16	7		.02	.05
12. Th. per 1	16	20	25		.02	
13. IL	107	179	93			.02
14. EL	1252	1376	1091			

[a] All time measures are in seconds
[b] Abbreviation for $B6D2F_1$

From: McGILL, T. E., and BLIGHT, W. C. 1963. The sexual behavior of hybrid male mice compared with the sexual behavior of males of the inbred parent strains. *Animal Behav.* 11: 480–483.

14 behavioral measures used in these studies. Of these, 10 show reliable differences between the two parent strains. For example, *ML* represents mount latency. This is the length of time after the female is put in the test cage before the male shows his first mounting reaction. An interstrain difference in the rapidity of response is indicated.

Like the rat, the male mouse achieves intromission several times before he reaches sexual climax or ejaculation. As shown in this table, the average number of intromissions in one strain was 17 and in another strain it was 5.

Other measures are self-explanatory and some are not important for our present purpose (although they are most important to Dr. McGill and, I presume, to the mice). The points I want to make are, (1) McGill has shown that there are behavioral differences between strains which are known to differ genotypically, and (2) when he crosses these strains he finds differences in the F_1 generation. By selectively backcrossing the hybrids to the parental stocks he can do more extensive genetical analyses. It is possible that with this technique one might identify the locus of the particular hereditary units involved.

HORMONES AND SEXUAL BEHAVIOR

My next topic has to do with gonadal hormones and sexual behavior. Instead of describing the effects of castration and subsequent administration of androgens or estrogens, I want to mention some relatively new developments that bear upon the problem of where, when, and how the so-called sex hormones have their effects.

We can approach this problem from a developmental point of view and thereby mesh with some points Dr. Money mentioned in Chapter 1. First, it is worthwhile to recall that gonadal hormones have long been known to exert specific effects upon the embryonic reproductive tract. The classic example is the freemartin. This is a female calf that has a twin brother. By reason of abnormalities in the prenatal blood supply, substances circulating in the male can pass into the vascular system of his female twin. Since the testes of the male fetus secrete androgen, the female is subjected to androgenic stimulation in the course of embryonic development. One result is that her external genitalia are greatly modified and in many respects resemble those of a male. There are additional indications of masculinization in the sex accessories.

In the early days of experimental embryology many studies were conducted to investigate the prenatal effects of gonadal hormones. In general, the results indicated that the differentiation and growth of the Wolffian ducts which give rise to much of the male reproductive apparatus depend upon stimulation by androgenic substances. In contrast, the Mullerian system, which provides the basis for female structures such as the fallopian tubes, the uterus, and vagina, undergoes normal development in the absence of gonadal secretions. Now, this is something that Dr. Money called to your attention: for development of the male system androgen is necessary; for the female system no sex hormone is needed.

Dr. Money discussed the occurrence of human intersexes, so-called hermaphrodites, and there is no question that at least some of these cases have been affected by endocrinological abnormalities. But Dr. Money stressed something more than morphology. He talked about psychological variables, early experience and the like, all of which I suppose can properly be subsumed under the general heading of behavior, and this is what I want to discuss in connection with experiments on animals.

A great deal of the credit for recent development of interest in the behavioral effects of hormones acting before birth belongs to Professor W. C. Young and his co-workers (see Chapter 9). The basic procedure consists of injecting pregnant guinea pigs with androgen or estrogen at a specific stage in gestation. The most interesting results pertain to the effects of testosterone on the female fetus. These females are ovariectomized soon after birth. When they reach adulthood they are injected with a combination of ovarian hormones known to produce sexual receptivity in spayed females that have not been exposed to androgen in the embryonic period. The experimental guinea pigs are strikingly unresponsive to the exogenous hormones. Many animals fail to become recep-

MATING BEHAVIOR IN ANIMALS   125

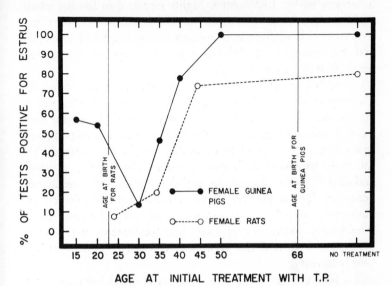

Figure 3. Sensitivity to estrogen as a function of androgen treatment at different ages post fertilization. From: William C. Young, The organization of sexual behavior by hormonal action during the prenatal and larval periods in vertebrates. In Frank A. Beach (Ed.), *Sex and behavior.* New York: Wiley, in press.

tive, and the remainder show sluggish or attenuated mating responses to the male.

Figure 3 illustrates the fact that the effects of androgen depend on the age of the fetus at the time of treatment. The age at treatment is indicated on the abscissa, and values on the ordinate indicate the percentage of tests in adulthood in which hormone administration produced sexual receptivity. Reading from right to left it is apparent that androgen injected at the fiftieth day of the sixty-eight–day gestation period has no effect upon the tendency to display sexual receptivity in adulthood. In contrast, females exposed to androgen at thirty days gestational age show very little mating behavior as adults.

In other experiments Young and his co-workers have treated female rats with androgen and obtained results comparable to those yielded by work on guinea pigs. The major difference is that treatment is highly effective in the rat when androgen is administered at birth. The difference between the two species is undoubtedly related to the length of gestation and the consequent difference in the stage of maturation reached at the time of birth.

Other workers have studied this same phenomenon. The report of Barraclough and Gorski is quoted in Chapter 1. Harris and Levine (1962) also reported that female rats treated with androgen on the day of birth never became receptive when they reached adulthood. It might be assumed that the early treatment with androgen had affected the pituitary and that therefore the ovaries failed to produce the hormones necessary for receptivity. However these workers injected experimental females with estrogen and progesterone, which would have produced receptivity had the females merely been ovariectomized, and this treatment did not reproduce receptive behavior.

The evidence thus suggests that gonadal hormones may exert part of their control over sexual behavior by directing the early differentiation and development of central nervous mechanisms which will mediate mating behavior in adulthood. In other words, certain behavioral differences between males and females may be related to differences in the CNS that are partly genetically controlled and partly due to the influence of hormones acting during the developmental period.

It is appropriate here to add some comments about the effects of gonadal hormones in adult animals. A question raised repeatedly is where and how these hormones exert their influence. One general assumption has been that they take effect in the CNS; that they may influence behavior by changing erotic excitability. Fuzzy notions of that sort have been advanced by a number of people, including myself. It has sometimes been argued that the gonadal steroids cannot pass the blood-brain barrier and therefore cannot affect the brain. The answer is that systemically administered steroids can and do pass this barrier, and that some gonadal hormones can act directly upon the brain.

One of the earliest relevant reports was that of Kent and Liberman (1949), dealing with the effects of ovarian hormones on sexual behavior in female golden hamsters. It was already known that such animals can be made sexually receptive by injecting them with an estrogenic hormone and following this with one injection of progesterone. Ordinarily the hormones are given intramuscularly or subcutaneously, and several hours must elapse between the progesterone injection and the onset of behavioral estrus. Kent and Liberman injected progesterone into the lateral brain ventricle and found that estrous responses appeared within one hour.

In 1956 Fisher published a brief but interesting report to the effect that sodium testosterone sulfate applied directly to the lateral hypothalamus of male rats produced the prompt appearance of intense masculine sexual behavior and, paradoxically enough, it also evoked maternal behavior on the part of males. More recently Fisher has suggested that this combination of male sex behavior and maternal behavior might have been brought about because the injection was made between two important centers (Fisher, 1960). Fisher has also stated that if he injects Versene in the brain, he obtains the same effect that is produced by androgen. This is important because Versene is not a hormone; it is a chelating agent that removes metallic ions. If this preliminary finding is verified by systematic experimentation it will be necessary to consider the possibility that hormonal effects on the brain do not involve stimulation, but may consist of removing chemical blocks and permitting the transmission of impulses from one center or system to another.

Another experiment which must be mentioned is that of Harris, Michael and Scott (1958). These workers used estrogen in a solid state. Crystals of stilbestrol were fused to the tip of a fine needle that could be permanently implanted at any desired location within the brain. Special tests revealed that the hormone diffuses only a short distance into the surrounding neural tissue. Nevertheless, when the implant was made in the dorsolateral hypothalamus of spayed cats sexual receptivity appeared within a few days. The same amount of hormone implanted in other brain regions or injected intramuscularly did not produce this effect. I have perhaps oversimplified the findings somewhat, and they yield no information concerning the mode of hormone action; but they do clearly point to certain hypothalamic regions as primary areas of involvement.

The most recently developed method of investigating localization of hormonal action, or at least hormone accumulation, involves the use of estrogen tagged with C^{14}. Michael (1962) implanted pellets of radioactive diethylstilbestrol in cat brains and made autoradiographic studies to study the extent of local spread of the hormone material. Even after long periods of implantation the distribution of active substance did not extend more than 400–600 microns beyond the edge of the implant site. There was some evidence indicating that certain neurons possess a selective, biochemical affinity for estrogen and these may well represent units in the neural mechanism which mediates receptive behavior.

The tagged hormone can of course be administered systemically and after varying periods of delay, different tissues can be examined by autoradiography and isotopic gas analysis to determine the concentration of radioactive material. Such analysis has revealed that in female cats levels of activity rise rather rapidly in blood, fat, muscle, and so on, and then begin to decline after two hours or so. In contrast, samples taken from sex-accessory tissues such as the uterus and vagina show much greater concentrations of radioactive estrogen, which reach a maximum approximately ninety-two hours after injection. Of greatest interest for students of behavior is the finding that the tagged hormone passes into the brain and accumulates in certain regions but not in others. Even with systemic administration maximal concentrations are found in restricted parts of the hypothalamus, which are the same loci that other techniques have implicated as being intimately involved in the estrogenic facilitation of mating behavior (Michael, 1963).

BRAIN FUNCTION AND SEXUAL BEHAVIOR

In discussing hormonal factors contributing to sexual performance I have unavoidably anticipated my final topic, which deals with brain function and mating behavior. The inextricable relationship between these problem areas is nicely illustrated by studies of localized changes in electrophysiological activity within the brain associated with changes in endocrinological condition or with the occurrence of certain hormone-dependent behavioral responses. One of the first such studies was reported in 1954 by Green, who recorded activity occurring in the anterior hypothalamus of female rabbits. He found that an increase occurred during mating behavior. Comparable changes were evoked in estrous rabbits by stimulating the vagina with a glass rod. It is important that Green got this result only when the females were in estrus and the estrogen level was high.

Immediately after mating the female cat shows a stereotyped behavior pattern known as the after-reaction. She disengages from the male, throwing him off if necessary, rolls over and over, squirming and twisting, and at intervals vigorously licks her vaginal area. Porter, Cavanaugh, Critchlow, and Sawyer (1957) implanted electrodes in the hypothalamus and recorded bursts of high amplitude activity that coincided with spontaneous display of after-reactions and could be artificially produced by mechanically stimulating the vagina of the receptive female.

These findings are particularly interesting when considered in conjunction with Fisher's report that injections of androgen into the lateral hypothalamus produce mating reactions in male rats. Other experiments reported from Sawyer's laboratory have shown that there are marked changes in neural activity within the preoptic region of female rabbits at the time of ovulation. This seems important because studies of labeled hormones indicate that the preoptic region is one of the brain areas in which injected estrogen accumulates (Michael, 1963).

It is of course essential that we learn everything possible about CNS activity associated with sexual performance in males as well as females. In my laboratory George Burt has been implanting electrodes in the various parts of the brain in male rats and recording activity before, during, and after sexual behavior. The work has just begun, but already there are indications that certain kinds of sexual reactions are accompanied or followed by orderly changes in neural activity in

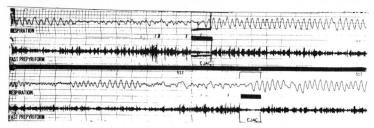

Figure 4.　Respiration and electrical activity from the prepyriform cortex of two male rats before, during, and after ejaculation (activity ranges between 30 and 35 CPS)

some systems and not in others. A single example will illustrate my point. As shown in Figure 4, Burt's records, taken from the prepyriform cortex, reveal that activity between 30 and 35 CPS is appreciably attenuated at the moment of sexual climax while the male is ejaculating. Very shortly thereafter discharges from this same region begin to occur in rhythmic bursts. The bursts correlate nicely with the slow, regular respiratory rhythm which characterizes the male rat's postejaculatory rest period.

We have similar records from several males. They seem to be reliable and repeatable but at the moment we do not know how to interpret them. Nevertheless, the fact that we can get consistent results is heartening. It encourages us to push on with investigation of other brain structures, including the hippocampus and hypothalamus. For the moment I am perfectly content to know that in the male as in the female, coital behavior is accompanied by predictable changes in the neurophysiological activity of certain brain regions.

One counterpart of brain recording is brain stimulation, but there have been very few experiments that involved stimulating the brain and observing sexual activity in male or female animals. According to Vaughan and Fisher (1962) stimulation of the dorsolateral hypothalamus in male rats accelerates mating and the occurrence of ejaculation. Karinen and Law (1958) have reported that female rats in diestrus will permit copulation by the male when electrical stimulation is applied to the hypothalamus. There are other reports to suggest that isolated elements of the male's mating pattern can be evoked by brain stimulation. Thus, MacLean and his coworkers (MacLean and Ploog, 1962) have produced penile erection in squirrel monkeys by stimulating the septal, hippocampal, and cingulate areas.

Along similar lines Herberg (1963) has found that by stimulating male rats in the area of the median forebrain bundle he can elicit seminal emission. The emission usually occurs without erection and without any of the other signs of a complete ejaculation that have been produced by copulation. Electrically induced emission is not accompanied by any indication of sexual arousal, and the brain stimulus has no apparent effect upon the male's behavior toward an estrous female.

Published findings concerning brain stimulation and sexual reflexes are tantalizingly fragmentary, but they arouse my optimism because it should be a relatively easy and straightforward task to combine the techniques with others for measuring mating behavior and thus advance our knowledge of the ways in which activity in the CNS is related to sexual phenomena.

CONCLUSIONS

I began this presentation with the statement that research on sexual behavior is in a phase of rapid expansion. New techniques are being applied, new data are being collected, new points of view are emerging. I hope that the evidence I have had time to present in highly condensed form will convince you that substantial progress is being made.

It is too early to discern precisely what direction this progress eventually will take, but as one who has watched the development of this field for more than twenty-five years I am optimistic that we are on the verge of important discoveries, new insights, valuable syntheses, and productive theoretical formulations.

SUMMARY

Recent advances in the study of sexual behavior have been made on four major fronts. The first of these has to do with relationships between sexual behavior and the evolution-

132   BEACH

ary process and includes study of ways in which evolution has
affected behavior and vice versa. The second concerns the investigation of genetical determinants of sexual performance.
Work in this area includes the detection and measurement of
behavioral differences in various strains and subspecies. It also
involves selective breeding for particular behavioral characters.
The third area of advance centers upon the effects of gonadal
hormones. It becomes increasingly clear that certain hormones
act as organizing agents early in development, influencing the
functional characteristics of neural mechanisms which later
will mediate adult mating behavior. Other work reveals that
the behavioral effects of hormones involve strictly localized
responses in certain brain regions. Finally, techniques permitting continuous recording from selected areas of the brain
or the application of stimuli to restricted brain regions have
yielded important information concerning ways in which the
central nervous system controls and directs sexual behavior.

REFERENCES

BLAIR, W. F.   1956   Call difference as an isolating mechanism in
southwestern toads (*Genus Bufo*). *Texas J. Sci.* 8, 87–106.
DOBZHANSKY, T.   1941   *Genetics and the origin of species* (ed.
2). New York: Columbia Univ. Press.
EISENBERG, J. F.   1962   Studies on the behavior of *Peromyscus
maniculatus gambelii* and *Peromyscus californicus parasiticus.*
Behaviour 29, 177–207.
FISHER, A. E.   1956   Maternal and sexual behavior induced by
intracranial chemical stimulation. *Science 124*, 228–229.
FISHER, A. E.   1960   Behavior as a function of certain neurobio-
chemical events. In *Current trends in psychological theory.*
Pittsburgh: Univ. Pittsburgh Press.
GODFREY, J.   1958   The origin of visual isolation between bank
voles. *Proc. royal physical Soc.*, Edinburgh 27, 47–55.
GREEN, J. D.   1954   Electrical activity in hypothalamus and
hippocampus of conscious rabbits. *Anat. Rec. 118*, 304.
GRUNT, J. A., and YOUNG, W. C.   1952   Differential reactivity of
individuals and the response of the male guinea pig to
testosterone propionate. *Endocrinology 51*, 237–248.
HARRIS, G. W., and LEVINE, S.   1962   Sexual differentiation of
the brain and its experimental control. Proc. physiol. Soc., in
J. Physiol. 163, 42–43P.
HARRIS, G. W., MICHAEL, R. P., and SCOTT, P. P.   1958   Neurological site of action of stilboestrol in eliciting sexual behavior.

In *Ciba foundation symposium on the neurological basis of behavior.* Boston: Little, Brown.

HERBERG, L. J. 1963 Seminal ejaculation following positively reinforcing electrical stimulation of the rat hypothalamus. *J. comp. physiol. Psychol. 56,* 679–685.

KARINEN, P., and LAW, T. 1958 Changes in sexual behavior in female rats following subcortical electrical stimulation. *Amer. Psychologist 13,* 408 (abstract).

KENT, G. G., JR., and LIBERMAN, M. J. 1949 Induction of psychic estrus in the hamster with progesterone administered via the lateral brain ventricle. *Endocrinology 45,* 29–32.

KNIGHT, G. R., ROBERTSON, A., and WADDINGTON, C. H. 1956 Selection for sexual isolation within a species. *Evolution 10,* 14–22.

McCLEARN, G. E., and RODGERS, D. A. 1961 Genetic factor in alcohol preference of laboratory mice. *J. comp. physiol. Psychol. 54,* 116–119.

McGAUGH, J. L., WESTBROOK, W., and BURT, G. 1961 Strain differences in the facilitative effects of 5-7 diphenyl-1-3-diaza-damantan-6-01 (1757 LS) on maze learning. *J. comp. physiol. Psychol. 54,* 502–505.

McGILL, T. E., and BLIGHT, W. C. 1963 The sexual behavior of hybrid male mice compared with the sexual behavior of males of the inbred parent strains. *Animal Behav. 11,* 480–483.

MacLEAN, P. D., and PLOOG, D. W. 1962 Cerebral representation of penile erection. *J. Neurophysiol. 25,* 29–55.

MARLER, P., and TAMURA, M. 1962 Song "dialects" in three populations of white-crowned sparrows. *Condor 64,* 368–377.

MAYR, E. 1942 *Systematics and the origin of species.* New York: Columbia Univ. Press.

MICHAEL, R. P. 1962 Estrogen sensitive neurons and sexual behavior in female cats. *Science 136,* 322.

MICHAEL, R. P. 1963 Hormonal control of sexual behavior. Program of the Eighth International Ethological Conference, Leiden, Holland.

PEARCE, STELLA 1960 An experimental study of sexual isolation within the species *Drosophila melanogaster. Animal Behav. 8,* 232–233.

PORTER, R. W., CAVANAUGH, E. B., CRITCHLOW, B. V., and SAWYER, C. H. 1957 Localized changes in electrical activity of the hypothalamus in estrous cats following vaginal stimulation. *Amer. J. Physiol. 189,* 145–148.

RASMUSSEN, E. W. 1953 The relation between strength of sexual drive and fertility in rats, cocks and mice. XVth International Veterinary Congress, Stockholm.

ROE, ANNE, and SIMPSON, G. G. (Eds.) 1958 *Behavior and evolution.* New Haven: Yale Univ. Press.

ROSENZWEIG, M. R., KRECH, D., and BENNETT, E. L.   1960   A search for relations between brain chemistry and behavior. *Psychol. Bull.* 57, 476–492.

SAWYER, C. H.   1960   Reproductive behavior. In J. Field (Ed.), *Handbook of physiology.* (Vol. II, Sec. I, Neurophysiology, pp. 1225–1240). Baltimore: Williams and Wilkins.

TRYON, R. C.   1929   Genetics of learning ability in rats. *University of California publications in psychology 4,* 71–89.

VALENSTEIN, E. W., RISS, W., and YOUNG, W. C.   1955   Experiential and genetic factors in the organization of sexual behavior in male guinea pigs. *J. comp. physiol. Psychol. 48,* 397–403.

VAUGHAN, E., and FISHER, A. E.   1962   Male sexual behavior induced by intracranial stimulation. *Science 137,* 758.

WHALEN, R. E.   1961   Strain differences in sexual behavior of the male rat. *Behaviour 28,* 199–204.

YOUNG, W. C., GOY, R. W., and PHOENIX, C. H.   1964   Hormones and sexual behavior. *Science 143,* 212–218.

6

CRITIQUE AND DISCUSSION

Part 1

Dr. Nowlis and I agreed that we were to serve as what he called Rip Van Winkles, people who can set the proceedings of today against the atmosphere of twenty or thirty years ago in this area and hope to make you realize how very, very much more we know today than we did and how very much more possible it is to know than it used to be.

When I was doing my work in the 30's and 40's, this was a matter of great courage, and of being willing to pay a very great deal professionally for the kind of work that one did. Even so, there were several studies that I did in those years that I simply did not dare to publish. There was one study, for instance, of two nymphomaniacs who were also very good introspectors and quite verbal. It is a great pity that it is lost. I do not have clear enough notes or memory of it any more to complete it. Various other studies were simply impossible to publish because there was no place to publish them; no editor would accept them. As much as I did publish—and I am sure the Kinsey people and many others would agree with this

—as much as we did publish on sexuality cost us plenty! Today I think that the atmosphere of this meeting is a guarantee, a promise of a renascence, a great flowering of research, not only in these directions but in others as well. The papers all pointed to some kinds of work that should be done in the future that would be very hard to do because of the cultural pressures of today. I can add a few that I would like to recommend as soon as it is possible to do them without too great social or personal cost.

One thing missing, not only in this meeting but in the whole of the sexological literature, is a good set of phenomenological studies. We simply do not have them. I wonder if there is a place to publish them; I wonder if it is possible to have studies of how it feels to be, let us say, in the situation of Dr. Masters' subjects. Or, more basically, we do not have a literature comparing one sexual, subjective consciousness with another. We do not have reports on how male or female sexuality feels to the particular person. We do not have such studies, so far as I know, on homosexuals or nymphomaniacs either. I think we are ready now to try to get the feeling, the consciousness, of what the sexual feeling is like from the inside.

I would particularly like to bring up the uncomfortable word that has not been mentioned here today, and should be, of course. It is well known that sexuality occasionally has some relationship to love. I feel very strongly that the phenomenological approach is one way in which we will discover the difference between the biological-sexual response, the kind of responses which are undoubtedly there, as we are hearing today, but which have a very different kind of flavor, as this audience must well know, from the sexual response in the affectionate, loving, personal relationship.

I would refer you here to a paper that I found extremely impressive by Judd Marmor, a psychoanalyst. It has just been reprinted in a book edited by M. DeMartino (1963), a collection of papers called *Sexual Behavior and Personality Characteristics*. Marmor's paper is in that book. I recommend it very highly on this question, which cannot truly be approached at the biological level alone or at the purely behavioral level alone—that is, the relationship, in the female, between what has been called the clitoral and the vaginal orgasm. If you interview women and get their sexual histories, they stick to this differentiation. You cannot talk them out of it, biology or no biology. These are differentiations for which Marmor has a very nice explanation at the clinical level.

Another function Dr. Nowlis and I can serve, being less involved in current research—after paying our respects to these excellent and even remarkable presentations we have heard today—is to try to place them in a more general, more inclusive picture of our present knowledge of sexuality and all its personality involvements. I am not saying this very well—let me say it this way: it is very easy when you get absorbed with a particular research to overgeneralize it. You tend to project it on too large a screen, to project too much, to make it over-important, to use it as a model, and so on.

I would like to mention some of the interesting kinds of knowledge and interesting kinds of research, starting from general and then going to the more specific, that I think would help us to put these four remarkable presentations—which, however, I would say are all partial presentations—into their proper place in a total integration.

First, I would like to remind you that Freud was not mentioned today nor was the psychoanalytic method. I would like to underscore it more, and to say a little more about the kinds of information which are available from this other kind of operation, this other method, which can help us in constructing this larger picture of sexuality into which we can place these specific researches reported today.

For one thing (I'm sure this is going to involve the biggest argument), I would like to point out that the concept of instinct has been approached historically almost as if it were two separate words even though spelled in the same way. It has been approached on the one side from the biological, ethological, evolutionary point of view; but equally respectably, even though totally different as an operation, the concept of instinct has been approached in the Freudian style via the free association technique. I would say that we have learned a great deal about instinct in this second way too. It is a more subtle, a more intangible method, difficult to handle, difficult to observe; and yet it has generated a very specific view of the concept which, to my own satisfaction, I've been able to phrase (in a forthcoming paper) in terms of seventeen operational and testable criteria for judging whether a given need is instinctoid or not. This can be called a reconstructive biology. It is not the best technique in the world in principle, and yet for a long time it was the only one we had for trying to determine whether there was anything in the human psyche which could be called instinctive or instinct-like. If the concept of instinct is characterized as it is in all the other research literatures, especially with animals, then the human being has no instinct, certainly nothing like the kinds of things that were reported by Dr. Beach. They are just simply lacking. Yet, with this clinical technique, it is possible to come to a conclusion, very widely shared by practically all psychoanalysts, that if there is any instinct remnant, anything *like* an instinct, anything instinctoid (a word that I made up to express this quality of being *like* even if it isn't exactly the same as)—if there is anything instinctoid in the human being, we must recognize that it is different from animal instinct in at least two important senses.

To begin with, it's weak. If there is anything there, it is weak and subtle. Dr. Money's paper, for instance, affirmed that hormones do not mechanistically determine masculinity or the femininity of sexual role or the sexual life. I will claim that they *do* have an influence, even though this is weak and totally overwhelmed by the power of early imprinting. On clinical grounds it is plausible to say that hormones *do* have demonstrated, determinative influence on the human psyche, in the Therese Benedek (Benedek and Rubenstein, 1942) kind of research, even though it may not show up in behavior because there are other stronger determinants and because this determinant is so weak.

Today we would, I think, phrase the whole process of psychotherapy in the newer terms of finding the identity, finding the self. This discovery of who you really are, of your own identity, can be phrased in biological terms as discovering your temperamental bent—discovering the weak impulse-voices, discovering these very weak, constitutional pushes that are so easily overbalanced and overwhelmed and drowned out altogether by cultural pressures and by learning. What I am trying to say is: the fact of the determinant being lost at the surface is no indication that the determinant does not exist. To say it in another way, that Freud would have agreed with, I think: a pretty good characterization of psychoanalytic therapy is that it is a process of recovering the drowned-out biological identity. All the talk about robotization and the loss of individuality and so on can be phrased in such biological terms also: many human beings have lost the consciousness of their instinctoid urges, and it is quite a job to get them to become aware of their constitutionally preferred behavior, of this delicate instinctoid pushing in one direction rather than another. Any parent who has more than one child knows very well what I am talking about when I speak of constitutional and biological bent.

The second point that also seems clear about human instinctoid tendencies is that the urge, the instigation, the push, the motivation is separable in the human being from what we might call the motivated *behavior,* and also from the choice of goal objects. As we learned very fully today, the human homosexual can *learn* to choose a like sex partner. And yet the sexual instigation, and the love instigation or need, may even so be instinctoid. A constitutional or biological push, which is weak but is there, gets tied to particular kinds of behavior and to particular objects by learning.

We can learn something else from Freud and from the post-Freudians—after all, our symposium today could be called pre-Freudian. It is another nonbehavioral approach, and as usual, it is very hard to put into words. I would call it the use of sex as a language, as a means of communication, as a channel through which other impulses, other needs, other instigations can be expressed.

With several of my colleagues, I investigated this use of sex recently in the interrelationship between dominance and sexuality. I think we demonstrated quite well that sex is not always plainly and simply sex. The same overt behavior can be a means of expressing affection *or* hostility, dominance *or* subordination, even though the camera eye would see them all as the same. Sex behavior and fantasy can be a means of expressing one's relationship to another person on the strength-weakness continuum, or the older-younger continuum, or the father-boy continuum. Dreams or fantasies are so often sexual because sexuality is very visual, so to speak. It is, therefore, a very good way in which to make symbolic pictures, which can express very, very much more than a simple sexual urge.

I remember how much I learned from one boy who had an anesthetic penis—no doubt neurotically anesthetic. Even though he had no genital feeling at all, he nevertheless felt impelled by all sorts of impulses, cultural and personal, and so on, to go through the ordinary sexual life of a young man —of courting women, seducing women, having intercourse, making believe that he was having all sorts of enjoyment when the whole thing was absolutely without feeling. He seems to have fooled everybody. His behavior, as nearly as he could make out, was a perfectly good mimicking of sexual behavior. Something was missing, however. It is possible to ask this kind of person, "Why are you doing all this? There's no fun in it particularly. What does it express? What are you trying to say?" and get truthful answers. We could learn a great deal by going *behind* the behavior of frigid men and women.

Another kind of research that I think we are about ready for is the phenomenological study of sexuality as a trigger to transcendent experiences, mystical experiences, of sexuality as a sacred act, as a religious ceremony. I can report from my researches (which did not start with sex as such but were concerned simply with collecting peak experiences and transcendent experiences) that sex is, under the right circumstances, one of the paths to transcendent experiences. One question that I would certainly like to ask of Dr. Hooker is this: Do homosexuals in the "good relations" such as she described ever have peak experiences; do they ever have the experiences of sacredness, of holiness, of ecstasy—that is, the kind of thing which is occasionally reported in the love relationships of normal people?

One methodological point is obviously suggested by Dr. Masters' amazing presentation (amazing to me at least because I had never read Dr. Masters' work as I had the work of the other speakers today), as I compare his findings and his procedures with the problems that I went through in trying to collect sexual histories, from both males and females. I also had started to collect sexual histories from males, expecting of course, that it would be easier than with females. But I too got into difficulties with boastfulness and therefore with unreliable data. To my surprise, I found that females were far more honest and open. I will not say exhibitionistic; I would say rather less involved with self-esteem. That is, it is easier for women to talk about these things because their self-esteem is less involved, less threatened by sexual "success" or "failure."

One of the findings this led me to is what I finally named volunteer error. While I was collecting subjects, I was at the same time working up a paper and pencil test of dominance feeling (or self-esteem) in the human female that made a verbal parallel with the behavior of subhuman primates. When I had worked this up and standardized it and then tested my sources of sexual histories, I found that I had almost entirely high-dominance subjects, and that I had missed half of the population. When I became aware of this, I then went deliberately for shyer people, for more delicate girls. I looked for the sweet girl rather than the strong one, the shy, the reserved girl, the more virginal character. These girls turned out to be less pagan about sexuality, more likely to identify sexuality almost entirely in a monogamous way with love for one person, very unpromiscuous and very unexperimental. I was able to demonstrate in a study made with Dr. Kinsey that the college students who volunteered and also showed up when Dr. Kinsey was on our campus were reliably higher in dominance feeling or self-esteem scores than the ones who did not show up. I had already demonstrated the strong correlations —in the order of .6 and in one case even .9—between a high-dominance test score and the pagan, bold, experimental sexual life. It was therefore demonstrated that volunteers for sexual researchers were reliably more promiscuous.

These findings suggest the possibility that high-dominance people would be more likely to submit themselves to Dr. Masters' kind of procedure. If you were to test the subjects that you have, Dr. Masters, I think you might very well find that they are reliably higher in dominance feeling than the people who refuse your solicitations, and that therefore your group masturbates more often than the average, that they will have had sexual experience with more partners, that they have pagan attitudes in general, that they will have certain kinds of sexual dreams, certain kinds of sexual fantasies, which I have described in print. In a word they might have a different kind of sexual life from the women and the men who have refused to be subjects for you.

This is not in any sense a refutation of the biological data. If you were able somehow to get these more shy and sensitive ones as subjects, there is no reason to expect that their biology would be any different. At this physiological level, there might be no difference. The difference might be at the psychological level only.

Perhaps one last generalization is about the scientific attitude and scientific approach that is possible in this kind of situation. I think it is obvious that Dr. Hooker's feelings for her subject are quite different from the kind of attitude that we traditionally call scientific. This is a more involved attitude, more the *encounter* that the existentialists talk about, than the detached and cool and stand-offish and objective kind of technique of being rather remote from the data instead of getting involved with them. It is our standard, our classical feeling as scientists, that we can do better if we are not emotionally involved. This I would like to question. I think there are certain kinds of data and certain kinds of researches —again, like the psychoanalytic, for instance—certain kinds of truth, where involvement with the data is better. With certain other kinds of truth, of course, involvement with the data is worse. I suggest that we will have to think very seriously of the implications of what I once heard Konrad Lorenz say, "If you want to learn *all* about ducks, you'd better like ducks."

REFERENCES

BENEDEK, THERESE & RUBENSTEIN, B. B.   1942   *The sexual cycle in women; the relation between ovarian function and psychodynamic processes*. Psychosomatic Medicine Monographs, Vol. 3, #1, #2. Washington: National Research Council.

DeMartino, M. F. (Ed.). 1963 *Sexual behavior and personality*. New York: Citadel Press.

Maslow, A. H., Rand, H., & Newman, S.   1960 Some parallels between the dominance and sexual behavior of monkeys and the fantasies of patients in psychotherapy. *J. nerv. ment. Dis. 131*, 202–212.

Maslow, A. H., & Sakoda, J.   1952 Volunteer-error in the Kinsey study. *J. abnorm. soc. Psychol. 47*, 259–262.

REBUTTAL—FRANK A. BEACH

Dr. Maslow's remarks are of historical interest and serve to set today's program in illuminating perspective. For a very long time it was generally asserted and believed that sexual behavior could not be studied with the same objective and quantitative methods that have proven fruitful in the investigation of human perception, learning, development and so on. The very essence of sexuality was elusive and undefinable, or else so deeply buried in the subconscious as to be inaccessible. (Dr. Maslow has spoken of weak urges, pushes, instinctoid motivations that have to be uncovered.) People were preoccupied with problems concerning the relative roles of the Id, Ego and Superego in human sex life. Matters weren't improved by additional uncertainty regarding conflict or interaction between the subconscious, the preconscious and the conscious.

Attempts to approach an understanding of sexual behavior from less confused starting points were not viewed favorably or sympathetically. Kinsey's monumental study was frequently criticized because it dealt with what people do and not how they feel. One negative comment which presumably was intended to be quite devastating was that the word "love" is never mentioned in the Kinsey Report. (Dr. Maslow echoes a need for love today.) Some detractors allowed that the Kinsey group had collected a useful body of factual information, but the data were regarded as biased and incomplete because so much had been left out. The really important information was that concerning unconscious motivation, supragenital aspects of sex, etcetera.

Now it seems to me Dr. Maslow is saying that what

the four speakers have presented today may be all well and good *as far as it goes,* but that there is much more to sexual behavior than we have brought out. Precisely what the residue may be is not clear to me (references to sexuality as a trigger to transcendental experiences add no illumination) but, in any event, no one has laid claim to an all-inclusive treatment or understanding of our central topic.

I am tremendously impressed and encouraged by the data and points of view that have been presented. They should convince anyone who still needs convincing that the sexual behavior of any species can be studied quantitatively, interpreted objectively, and generally dealt with in the same operational framework that has been successfully employed in the investigation of other complex, interpersonal activities.

If Dr. Maslow prefers to emphasize and extol an approach based upon "instinctoid" urges and unconscious conflicts, that is his privilege, and I wish him success (though how he will recognize and communicate success escapes me). For my part, I will place my faith in the kind of work and intellectual orientation represented by Drs. Hooker, Money, and Masters. That way, I believe, lies the real promise of scientific advance and understanding.

REJOINDER—ABRAHAM H. MASLOW

I will not be pushed into the position that I do not want to defend, of dichotomizing careful scientific work from speculative, theoretical, Daniel Boone-type reaching out to the future. I love them both, I have done them both, and by the way, Frank Beach has done them both too. But it is a dangerous thing to think that we are being unscientific when we poke our fingers out, when we try to become aware of what is yet to be done—of what may yet be missing, of what is available to us in common experience which has not yet been handled scientifically—and when we set this up in the form of questions, of hypotheses, and of probing out into the future.

It is part of the strategy of science, to try to know where to put your money, where to put your time. We don't have infinitely long lives. Any experiment means a considerable in-

vestment of time, not to mention libido. You choose that wh\
seems most promising, most important, most likely to bri\
the kind of satisfaction that you would like.

The argument is an old story between Frank and me; we've engaged in it long before now, because I enjoy speculating more than he does. I think that he, in fact, feels guilty when he speculates. Yet, I know that he must because of so many good experiments which did not come out of his left ear. They must have come out of thinking and planning and trying to decide the best way to go—in this direction or in that direction? It was not just pebble collecting he was occupied with; it was not just blind, random picking up facts. It was guided by theory, and theory means sitting and thinking and talking and so on.

More scientists, I think, are apt to do this planning and gambling in private—in the bar, or over a bottle of bourbon. I think it is well to do it in public, especially for our young people. Otherwise the undergraduate and the graduate student get phoney notions about science, as if it all came wrapped up in paper, wrapped around with ribbon, and somehow completed. They have little notion of the kind of stumblings and the dreams and the fantasies and the waking up in the middle of the night; and the arguments and the changes of minds and vacillations and the mistakes that are part of the process of getting up to the point where you know enough to be able to plan a good, controlled experiment.

I would say this very flatly: I think you have to know a hell of a lot before you can do a good experiment. A good experiment is a kind of last stage in knowledge. That's the point where you can put a true or false question to Nature. Well, you had *better* know a lot before you commit yourself to an experiment or you are just going to do foolish experiments!

These first stages in the development of that knowledge— this is what I was trying to talk about. I was trying to speak specifically about clinical data that *are* data, however hard it is to quantify them—though even this is being accomplished. It is very difficult but it is possible. Further, even prequantitative data also are still data. If you have been a psychotherapist yourself and if you have experienced, time and again, certain happenings, and if you find it difficult to put them into words, you finally may wind up with metaphors, perhaps. Now, this is not at the same level of reliability as the kind of data that you will get after you have been working five or six or seven years, when you are then able to design a crucial experiment; but these *are* data. If they are less reliable than the experimental data, they are still data.

I would maintain that it is from this same pool that I was talking about—the psychoanalytic, the Freudian, the psychodynamic pool—that a very, very large proportion of the experimental work in psychology took its origins. Much that we heard today came out of those prescientific speculations. Therefore, I don't want to get pushed into a fight because I do not think there is any. I have admired tremendously the kind of work that we have heard presented, but my effort today is to put it into the context of: Where do we go from here? What kind of work do we do next year and the year after? What is missing? What are the warnings that the man on the sidelines, the more detached person can give to the person who is involved in a particular set of data? These are real questions that have been raised and not phoney questions, and had better be listened to.

7

CRITIQUE AND DISCUSSION

Part 2

You already know that both your discussants are Rip Van Winkles of sex research. Both Dr. Maslow and I investigated animal sex behavior in the thirties and went on to study human sex behavior before becoming interested in other problems, such as our mutual current concern with research on phenomena to which terms like consciousness are applied. Here we are, called back to examine and comment on these excellent presentations of studies in the enormously important domain of sex research. Well, how do things look to me?

I

My first comment concerns progress in sex research at the human level and is in response to Dr. Beach's plea to this audience to remember that not all the work is on the human and that there are indeed many investigators of animal sex behavior. It does seem only yesterday that the plea we heard was for more first-rate investigations of human rather than animal sex behavior. In 1954, for example, William Young assembled at the Lord Jeffrey Inn at Amherst the following for an informal three-day symposium on sex research: Beach, Brady, Buxton, Corner, Dempsey, Freedman, Gebhard, Goy, Grunt, Joan Hampson, Kagan, Kinsey, Kubie, Leathem, McKenzie, Money, Nissen, Nowlis, Plough, Pomeroy, Rioch, Riss, Rock, Rogers, Rosenblatt, Rosvold, Sawin, Stone, Valenstein, and Wislocki. One of the persistent themes of that conference was a general pessimism about the possibility of doing truly significant sex research with the human in our time. Seldom has a conclusion by such a distinguished panel been proven to be wrong in such a short time. For in that very year, Dr. Masters established his Sex Research Project at Washington University, Dr. Hooker began the research reported here today, and Dr. Money, who had recently completed his doctoral dissertation on hermaphroditism, began to report his work with the Hampsons and others on the independent factors in sexual differentiation.

But important pressures against sex research are still present today. If Kinsey could say at that 1954 symposium, "The right to do sex research at the human level has not been established," we can say a decade later that that right has not yet been completely established. For example, in contemplating the amazing achievements of Dr. Masters and the courage, intelligence, and integrity required to reach them, one wonders why psychological measures were not used simultaneously with the other measures. When subjects come repeatedly to the laboratory for research in which complex emotional responses are aroused and feelings released in the presence of a respected professional investigator, it is essential to seek an understanding of the meaning to the subject of these responses, of this situation, of this investigator, and of this research, and an understanding of changes in these meanings with repeated experience. The psychological data secured in this situation would not only be significant for the psychologist but would also be indispensable for a complete understanding of the anatomical and physiological data. Were these data not obtained because someone decided that while it might be all right for a gynecologist to poke around in the pelvis he should not peek at the person? Sponsors should continue to review critically their research policies lest they inadvertently exclude from the purview of the responsible investigator that which is of great potential importance to his work. Since behavioral scientists have shown again and again their willingness to resist social pressures against various kinds of socially significant behavioral research, I appeal to this large audience of the New England Psychological Association to note that there are still pressures to be identified and resisted in the domain of sex research.

II

Fragmentation of knowledge and poor communication in this area occur not only at the boundaries of the several scientific disciplines but also within any one discipline. I believe there are two important reasons why investigators of sex behavior particularly need to educate each other in long uninterrupted sessions like this one and like the three-day Amherst symposium.

The first reason arises from the fact that we are reared in a culture in which human sex behavior is not only highly private but is also embedded from infancy in a context of punishment, frustration, fear, and anxiety. The Kinsey series of histories suggested that scientists who engage in sex research on any species are no more free of anxieties and conflicts about sex than are other individuals. One scientist's particular pattern of defenses and of experience may prevent him from seeing items of sex behavior that appear obvious to another. Often it is only direct personal communication in the presence of the phenomenon that permits the scientist to revise his mode of perceiving it. I recall a leisurely visit in 1946 to the Primate Section of the St. Louis Zoo with Alfred Kinsey and Robert Yerkes. Both had been studying primate sex behavior for years and had communicated with each other many times, but this was the first time they had had an opportunity to discuss their observations at the moment they made them. Each observer noted as sex behavior many items which the other had either ignored or categorized differently.

A second reason for fragmentation and for poor communication is the careless application of dirty terms to the phenomena of sex behavior. I do not refer to the classic four-letter words but to supposedly objective and technical terms like copulation, orgasm, sex play, erotic arousal, and homosexuality. Each of these complex terms is typically soiled by various sins of omission and of commission. Just as the language analysts in modern philosophy have taught us to explicate a portmanteau term by unpacking it, by examining its many components, and by finding a central significant paradigm, operationalists like Frank Beach have correctly insisted through the years that we carefully search for and identify *all* the phenomena to which a term applies and then establish through further research the one most significant invariant way of defining that set of phenomena. Dr. Beach's present paper shows clearly how this methodological principle has led to increasingly significant research on sex. We have also seen and heard how the personal interactions in a leisurely meeting like this release not only heat but light as the principle and its implications are discussed. The New England Psychological Association is to be congratulated for maintaining the plan which led originally to its formation: that is, to have meetings for the sole purpose of providing long sessions of this kind.

III

One of the unexpected pleasures this Rip Van Winkle experienced in hearing these papers came through the convergence of Dr. Money and Dr. Hooker on the problem of psychosexual differentiation. One might conclude from some segments of the current literature that many are concerned about the problems of ego identity in American men and women but that few are doing basic research on these problems. Money and Hooker are, and in a most interesting way.

Through John Money's identification of different relatively independent factors in biological and psychological sexual differentiation we can move toward more thorough explication of the concepts of masculinity and femininity. To begin to see that chromosomal sex, hormonal sex, gonadal sex, morphological sex, gender role sex, and behavioral sex do not fuse into a monolithic male or female but function as interacting and even conflicting systems is to take a large forward step in

CRITIQUE AND DISCUSSION 151

understanding human nature. Also notable in his work is the tracing back of differentiated traits to their common origins. Thus, by attending to what is contemporaneously equivalent in male and female and to what is of common genetic origin, he provides us with a sounder basis for identifying that which is different between male and female.

It is interesting to note how our emphasis fluctuates. At times we are impressed with that which is different; at other times it is that which is equivalent in the two sexes which impresses. When I joined Dr. Kinsey's project at Indiana in 1944, he reviewed in a number of conferences the assumptions, methods, and data he expected to describe fully in a series of six or seven volumes. At that time the data on the male had been fairly thoroughly analyzed and a preliminary analysis of the female data had also been made. Kinsey was deeply impressed at that time by sex differences in sexual behavior; he often said that these differences were of such a large order that they would lead a taxonomist to wonder whether he should place the two sets of individuals in different species. When I saw him for the last time, ten years later at the Amherst symposium and after the appearance of the female volume, I asked him what he felt the most important contribution of his work would be. He immediately said it would be the research he hoped others would be stimulated to do by Part III of *Sexual Behavior in the Human Female*. Most of you know that the chapters in Part III definitely contradict many of his earlier expectancies about sex differences. He concludes Chapter 15, for example, by stating: "In spite of the widespread and oft-repeated emphasis on the supposed differences between female and male sexuality, we fail to find any anatomic or physiologic basis for such differences." In later chapters he does present "differences in the psychologic and hormonal factors which affect the responses of the two sexes," but he concludes that "males would be better prepared to understand females, and females to understand males, if they realized that they are alike in their basic anatomy and physiology" (p. 641).

Fortunately, these chapters have led, in part, to such important work as that presented in this symposium, work which is beginning to show that our cultural and scientific concepts of masculinity and femininity must be critically reviewed and revised. As Dr. Hooker indicates, what we have inherited is a mode of perceiving as masculine that which is active, dominating, possessing, controlling, and inserting; and as feminine, that which is passive, inactive, submissive, possessed, controlled, and receiving. These perceptions were derived, in part, from misunderstandings and unwarranted expectancies about male and female behavior in sexual intercourse and in other social interaction. When the focus of scientific attention is on the total organism, as in the Kinsey and Masters data, the traditional masculine–feminine dichotomy appears absurd. As modern woman discovers her full potential in the heterosexual situation, her physiological and anatomical response in intercourse is found by Kinsey to be importantly similar to that of the male and by Masters sometimes to surpass that of the male in vigor, intensity, and duration. Other behavioral components of gender role show similar lack of clear dichotomization. We cannot foresee which differences between the sexes will be identified, prescribed, and positively sanctioned in future cultural definitions of the masculine and of the feminine. Psychologists have a responsibility for the objective clarification of these concepts. One hopes that future cultural definitions, based on these objective studies, will include, as far as possible, only those traits which do not prevent the person who accepts this constraint from achieving his fullest possible development as a person.

Dr. Hooker's contribution to the study of psychosexual differentiation arises, paradoxically, from her study of homosexual behavior in the male. When the term homosexuality is applied by the layman to a particular individual there is often the vague implication that that individual necessarily deviates on a number of Dr. Money's factors: genetic ("born that way"), hormonal ("insufficiency of appropriate sex hormone"), morphological plus gender role ("effeminate," "mannish"), and sexual behavior ("attracted to the same sex"). Kinsey's thorough analysis of the concept of heterosexual–homosexual balance helped to establish that one of these factors (sexual behavior as erotic arousal plus instrumental acts leading to orgasm with a person of the same sex) was based in both males and females primarily on conditioning and learning and was thus, in principle, relatively independent of the other factors. The extensive data he secured that would help establish this independence have never been fully written up for publication, so far as I-know. Going beyond Kinsey through use of psychological interviews, tests, and observations and through careful attention to complex social learning in dyads and subcultures, Dr. Hooker now provides us with a very clear analysis of some of these independent but interacting factors.

She asks this question: "Irrespective of the degree to which the male homosexual fulfills the male gender role expectations in all other respects," how does he solve the problems associated with his failure, through erotic focus on other males, to be male in this important respect? In searching for answers to this question, Dr. Hooker has studied for eight years thirty males who were exclusively homosexual; only three had had heterosexual experiences, and these, "a maximum of three overt heterosexual experiences each." These three would be rated as 5 on the Kinsey heterosexual–homosexual scale, as she says, but let us note that this might be their rating only in the years in which those experiences occurred; indeed, they might have had a still lower rating in those particular years, depending on the relative amount of concurrent involvement with the homosexual. One of the advantages of the structure of the Kinsey interview was the specificity with which it attempted to get at the total pattern of sexual activity in each year of the life history, thus permitting estimates of an Ht–H rating and of other measures for each of those years. Some males who are 5's and 6's at age 25–57 may have had much lower ratings in some of their earlier years. That Dr. Hooker simply rates three men as 5's and the twenty-seven others as 6's suggests that their sexual behavior has been more or less exclusively homosexual throughout their lives. But she does not make this fully explicit. To move from lower ratings early in life to higher ratings later would give to the subject a different meaning of his homosexuality and a different basis for resolving his problem than would a history of high ratings throughout early life. Since the study began as a search for the developmental sequences leading to identification as an adult homosexual, we can anticipate that in later papers Dr. Hooker will examine these earlier patterns year by year.

Dr. Hooker clearly demonstrates how one's perception of the masculinity or femininity of his own sexual behavior varies in importance from individual to individual. As suggested earlier, this perception is based in part on arbitrary cultural formulations about masculinity–femininity; it is also based on notions about homosexuality and the way in which homosexuality and masculinity–femininity are interrelated. Twelve of Dr. Hooker's informants accept the attribution of masculinity (active, dominating, inserting) and of femininity (passive, submissive, receiving) to homosexual behavior. Only two of these show a resolution in which they believe they are fully masculine with respect to biological sex, gender role, and sexual behavior. The others illustrate various self-perceived incongruities among these components. All twelve, in accepting this particular aspect of the masculinity–femininity dichotomy, would expect that homosexual behavior necessarily involves incongruities for someone, since they would also believe that to be masculine in any sexual episode necessarily requires another male to be feminine.

But the seventeen men in her largest group, while accepting a general masculinity–femininity continuum for psychological attributes, a continuum on which they perceive themselves as more masculine than feminine, reject the masculinity–femininity dichotomy for sexual behavior itself. Each of these males shows variability in preference and performance, accepting from time to time both those items which the former group considers masculine and those items it considers feminine. Thus, even in a situation fraught with potentials for fear, anxiety, guilt, and shame, these informants learned to perceive the traditional masculinity–femininity dichotomy as irrelevant to sexual behavior. Since this is a mode of perception that is more nearly congruent than is the traditional mode with the data supplied by the Kinsey and Masters studies, we should investigate the incidence with which it occurs in individuals with other kinds of sexual histories. Are an increasing number of heterosexual partners in the security provided by marriage learning new expectancies about male and female roles in sex behavior? If the answer is positive, should we then ask the more general question: Are we moving toward a cultural situation in which the male who is confident of his masculinity can more readily develop much that is latent but now called feminine in his nature and the female similarly develop that which is now called masculine in hers?

Because of the manner in which Dr. Hooker's informants had to be selected, she does not project her quantitative findings (such as the proportion arriving at a particular solution of the gender role problem) to other subgroups. But the research problems she identifies in studying her sample do have very general application. In addition to the problem just discussed, I find of particular interest for a social psychology of sexuality her analysis of the learning of expectancies about homosexual behavior in different subgroups and her description of learning and adjustment in pairs who live together through the years.

IV

These four papers, in different ways, point to the continued need for more research on the early developmental processes involved in all aspects of psychobiological sexual differentiation. Such research is difficult for many reasons. Since the scientist is not free of his culture, and since our culture is particularly prohibitive with respect to sexuality in the child and to sexual interaction between adult and child, we find it almost impossible to be completely objective in this area. Freud was himself repeatedly distressed that his information led to the concept of infantile sexuality. Certainly many of us were also distressed about the nature of the observational situation when we first encountered on page 177 of *Sexual Behavior in the Human Male* the stop-watch data of "the technically trained persons who have kept diaries or other records . . . [with] information on 317 preadolescents (down to age two months) who were either observed in self-masturbation, or who were observed in sexual contacts with other boys or older adults."

A second difficulty arises from the extremely low frequency with which overt sexual acts are exhibited by children in our society. When the Sears, John Whiting, and I studied the development of aggressive and dependent behavior in preschool children in the Iowa Child Welfare Research Institute we tentatively included in the original observational schedule some categories of sexual behavior. These were soon dropped since no instances were observed either in the preschool setting or in a permissive doll-play test. Apparently such acts are also rare in the middle class home. In a long interview with each mother about her responses to problem-making behaviors in her children we included several opportunities to talk about sex behavior. The mothers' discourse was usually frank and sincere, but they had very little to say about sex behavior in their children and about problems of managing it. When a content analysis involving the Discomfort-Relief Quotient was made of the interview, their reported discomfort about sex behavior was lower than that for other categories of child behavior. Their reports never referred to erotic arousal, rarely referred to sex play, but did refer to warnings about going with strangers or playing with the children of certain families.

What these mothers did talk about at length in the general area of sex was the teaching of countless rules about modesty, appropriate language, and the many behavioral items that are differentially required or prohibited for boys and for girls. Moreover, in other observations, we found that even at the preschool level boys and girls use these rules about gender role in their control of each other. Similarly, Kinsey, who was an excellent interviewer of young children, found that at a very early age they have learned to discriminate between pictures of boys and of girls (sometimes on the basis of a simple cue like haircut), and that they can formulate, at least in part, how the rules for boy-girl play differ from those for play among boys and play among girls. Here, then, is the source of a third difficulty for research on the early development of psychosexual differentiae. Just as we have learned from research on personality development that sexual behavior itself inevitably acquires functional relationships with a great variety of nonsexual motivational systems, we have also learned that expectancies about sex in general involve an even greater variety of behavioral systems. Furthermore, the learning situation for each child is unique. Since these expectancies are part of the child's concept of his gender role, our difficulty is that of fully identifying them for any one child.

A great step forward toward meeting this difficulty is Dr. Money's conclusion that the critical period in the acquisition of a gender role and a psychosexual identity is "approximately simultaneous with the establishment of native language." With this as an anchor point, we can point to the need both for further research on how this role and identity are learned during the early critical period and for further research on how they relate to and interact with identification processes and identity formation later in life.

part two

8

THE EFFECT OF REARING
CONDITIONS ON BEHAVIOR *

A wealth of clinical evidence shows that human children who
have never had adequate maternal care or who have been
separated from adequate maternal care within some critical
stage, suffer disturbance and delay or even irreparable damage
in terms of subsequent personal-social development. The importance of maternal ministrations in the child's development
is further supported by many clinical investigations and by
some limited experimental data.

Personality malfunctions that have been attributed to
maternal inadequacy include such syndromes as marasmus,
hospitalism, infantile autism, feeble-mindedness, inadequate
maternal responsiveness, and deviant or depressed heterosexuality. If these disorders are the results of maternal inadequacy, only research with human subjects can establish the
conditions and kinds of maternal behavior that produce them.

---

* Presented to a forum of the Menninger School of Psychiatry, December
4, 1961.

Unfortunately, experiments critical to the resolution of these problems cannot be done with human subjects. We cannot rear babies in illuminated black boxes during the first half-year, year, or two years of their lives. We cannot have mothers rear their children in isolation from other children and from adults for the first two, four, or eight years. We dare not have human children reared with either no mothers or inadequate mothers while providing them with maximal opportunity to interact with age-mates, either identically reared or differentially reared. Yet these are the kinds of experiments which are required if we are to assess the effects of maternal variables unconfounded with other experiential variables on the child's personal-social development.

Most clinical investigations have given primary attention to the effects of maternal privation, defined as absence or inadequacy of maternal responsiveness, or to maternal deprivation, defined as infant separation after the infant has established profound, or at least adequate, maternal attachments. Relatively little attention has been given to the effects of the absence or inadequacy of opportunity for the child to interact with other children and to form adequate affectional patterns with and for them. We know that it is important for the child to form effective infant-mother affectional patterns, but it also is likely that he must form effective child-child affectional patterns if he is to attain normal personal-social, sexual, and parental patterns. Obviously these affectional systems are not independent. It is possible, but by no means a certainty, that at the human level, normal child-child affection requires previous affectional bonds between mother or mother-figure and child. It is certain that the mother plays an important role in the formation of peer affections by providing for and encouraging associations between infants or children, or by preventing or discouraging such associations. Human mothers may also markedly influence the nature and course of child-child relationships.

Psychoanalytic theory, which looks for temporal reduction and temporal primacy, will ascribe primary importance to the earliest causes and conditions whether or not these are of greatest importance. Initial traumas have a false clarity as causative agents since they are not confounded by preceding events, whereas the role of all subsequent events is confounded by the role of these events operating during previous experience. Yet primacy in time need not, and often should not, be equated with primacy in importance.

EFFECTS OF TOTAL SOCIAL DEPRIVATION ON MONKEYS

Six years ago we took two newborn rhesus monkeys, one male and one female, and subjected them to total social deprivation for the first two years of life. Each was placed in a solid, illuminated cage such that it never saw any other animal—monkey or human—even though it was tested for food responsiveness and learning by remote-control techniques. During isolation these monkeys adapted to solid food slowly and learned with great difficulty, but they were found to have normal weight and good coats when removed—there were no signs of marasmus. At the conclusion of the two years' isolation, they were tested for social responsiveness to each other and to normal monkeys smaller and younger than themselves. They did not respond to each other and either froze or huddled in a corner when abused by the younger animals. Placed together in a cage in a room with many caged monkeys, they showed withdrawal from this new external world, and in the more than two years they lived together, they remained abnormally frightened, showed minimal interaction, and engaged in no sex activities. In follow-up social tests at four years of age with smaller and weaker monkeys, they made no effort to defend themselves except for one brief episode with one of the pair, after which it curled into a ball and passively accepted abuse. The potential for social behaviors in these animals had apparently been obliterated.

We have preliminary, incomplete data on the effects of such total social deprivation confined to a six-month period and are obtaining other data on the effects of such deprivation over a twelve-month period. The results to date indicate severe but not complete withdrawal from external environmental stimulation. Repeated testing in our playroom situation, shown in Figure 1, reveals that one of these monkeys is almost totally

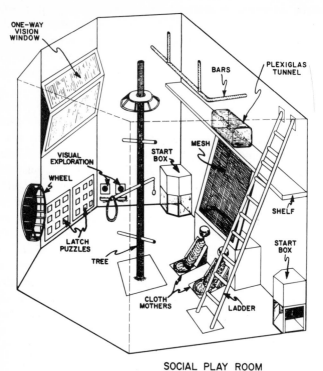

SOCIAL PLAY ROOM

Figure 1.

unresponsive socially and the other only occasionally engages in brief, infantile-type social interactions. Normally, the play-room is a highly stimulating situation for monkeys. It is 8 feet high with 36 square feet of floor space, and it contains multiple stationary and mobile toys and tools, flying rings, a rotating wheel, an artificial tree, a wire-mesh climbing ramp, and a high, wide ledge, offering opportunities to explore and play in a three-dimensional world.

We also have data on eight monkeys subjected to total social isolation from other monkeys during the first 80 days of life. Although they neither saw nor contacted nor heard other monkeys, they did see and contact human experimenters, who removed them from their isolation boxes and tested them repeatedly on learning problems after the second week of life. A year later these animals appear to be normally responsive to external environmental stimulation and they are socially responsive to each other when tested in the playroom. This social responsiveness as measured by the appearance of increasingly complex play patterns has become qualitatively normal, but probably it is depressed somewhat quantitatively. Whether there will be subsequent effects on heterosexual and maternal behavior remains for future observation.

If we assume a rough developmental ratio of four to one for monkey to man, the results on these eight monkeys are not completely in accord with human clinical data, which at best are only roughly comparable to our experimental situation. Social isolation up to eight or ten months of age is reported to endanger or impair the personal-social development of human infants. It may be that the stimulation and handling of the monkeys in the learning experiments played a positive role in preparing them for subsequent exposure to a monkey environment, thus minimizing the isolation effects. It is also possible that the human infant is more susceptible than the monkey infant to damage from social isolation.

EFFECTS OF EARLY PARTIAL SOCIAL DEPRIVATION

We have data on various groups of monkeys raised from the day of their birth without their mothers and without any monkey companionship at least through the first half-year. One group of 56, now ranging in age from five to eight years, was raised in individual bare wire cages where they could see and hear other monkeys, but not touch them. A group of four was similarly housed for up to five years, but had access to a single wire surrogate [1] during the first half-year of life. A third group of over 100 monkeys was raised identically except for access to a cloth surrogate [2] or to both a cloth surrogate and a

---

[1] A wire surrogate mother is a bare, welded wire cylindrical form surmounted by a wooden head with a crude face and supported semiupright in a wooden frame.

[2] A cloth surrogate differs from the wire surrogate in that the wire cylinder is cushioned with a sheathing of terry cloth.

wire surrogate during at least six months of the first year.[3] Approximately half of these animals have been housed after six months or one year of age with another monkey of like age and like or unlike sex for part or all the time since.

Although there may be differences in the personal-social behaviors of the monkeys comprising these groups, we cannot be sure at the present time, and for this reason we group them together. Many members of all three groups have developed what appear to be abnormal behaviors, including sitting and staring fixedly into space, repetitive stereotyped circling movements about the cage, clasping the head in the hands and arms while engaging in rocking, autistic-type movements, and intrapunitive responses of grasping a foot, hand, arm, or leg and chewing or tearing at it with the teeth to the point of injury.

The sex behavior of the six oldest wire-cage-raised monkeys was first measured by Mason[4] in 1960 and compared with that of rhesus monkeys of equal age which had lived in the wild during most of the first year of life. All the wild-raised monkeys, male and female, showed normal sex behavior, characterized in the male by dorsoventral mounting, clasping the legs of the female by the feet, and holding the buttocks by the hands. The females in turn sexually presented themselves by elevating their buttocks and tails, lowering their heads, and frequently looking backward without threatening. No laboratory-raised male or female showed normal sex behavior. Attempted mounting by the male was random in regard to body part, and the most frequent pattern was grasping a side of the female's body and thrusting laterally. The female's patterns were totally disordered and often involved sitting down and staring aimlessly into space. Although none of these animals was sexually mature, heterosexual positioning in both male and female normally develops during the second year.

Attempts to breed the cage-raised monkeys approxi-

---

[3] Harlow, H. F.: The nature of love. *Amer. Psychologist* 13:673–685, 1958. Harlow, H. F.: Love in infant monkeys. *Sci. Amer.* 200:68–74, 1959.

[4] Mason, W. A.: The effects of social restriction on the behavior of rhesus monkeys: I. Free social behavior. *J. comp. physiol. Psychol.* 53:582–589, 1960.

mately two years later also ended in complete failure. When the oldest wire-caged-raised females were between five and seven years of age and the oldest surrogate-raised females were between three and five years, repeated attempts were made to breed 11 of the wire-caged-raised females and four of the cloth-surrogate-raised females with highly selected males from our breeding colony. The females were placed in the large breeding cages during estrus, and if no fighting ensued within 15 minutes, they were left overnight. Eventually one wire-caged-raised female and three cloth-surrogate females became pregnant. Although observation did not reveal clear-cut differences in the behavior of these two groups, the differences in pregnancy approach significance in spite of—or possibly because of—the greater immaturity of the cloth-surrogate-raised females. Actually, no female, impregnated or not, demonstrated a normal pattern of sexual behavior. Many females tried to avoid the males; some actually threatened the males and would probably have been injured had our males not been carefully screened. When the males approached and positioned the females, the females usually collapsed and fell flat on the floor. Impregnation of the four females was achieved only through the patience, persistence, knowledgeability, and motor skill of the breeding males.

We have subsequently tested many wire-cage- and surrogate-mother-raised males and females with experienced breeding females and experienced breeding males, respectively, in a large 8-foot by 8-foot by 8-foot room especially designed for breeding studies. All the males have continued to show the disorganized and inappropriately oriented sexual responsiveness which we have already described, and no male has ever appropriately mounted our experienced and cooperative breeding-stock females, let alone achieved intromission.

With a single exception we have never seen normal, appropriate sexual posturing in our wire-cage- or surrogate-raised females. The females do not approach the males, nor do they groom or present. One cloth-surrogate-raised female was not impregnated throughout six mating sessions, and during this time she began to respond positively and appropriately to the males and eventually developed a normal, full-blown pattern of sexual presentation and sexual posturing during copulation.

EFFECTS OF MATERNAL CONDITIONS

Direct comparison of the effects of being raised by real monkey mothers and cloth surrogate mothers on subsequent personal-social development has been measured by the use of our playpen test situation. In two playpen situations babies were housed with their real mothers, and in a third setup the babies were housed with cloth mothers. The playpen, whose floor plan is given in Figure 2, consists of large living cages each housing a mother and an infant and adjoining a compartment of the playpen. A small opening in each living cage restrains the mother, but gives the infant continuous access to the adjoining playpen compartment. During two daily test sessions, each an hour in length, the screens between playpen compartments were raised, permitting the infant monkeys to interact as pairs during the first six months and as both pairs and groups of four during the second six months. Two experimenters independently observed and recorded the behavior exhibited during test sessions.

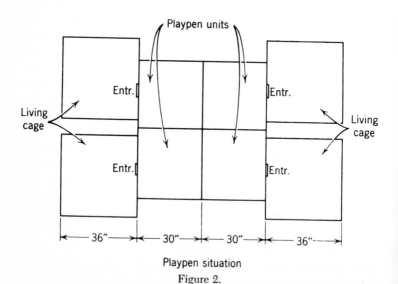

Playpen situation

Figure 2.

The infants raised by real monkey mothers were more socially responsive to each other than were the infants raised by the cloth surrogates. They showed a wider range of facial expressions, and, probably of paramount importance, they developed simple interactive play patterns earlier than the surrogate-raised monkeys and achieved a level of complex play patterns not achieved by the surrogate-raised monkeys during an 18-month test period.

All the male, mother-raised infants have at one time or another responded sexually toward the mother with pelvic thrusting and in at least two cases by dorsoventral mounting. In three cases pelvic thrusting to a female was observed before 50 days of age and in a fourth case, before 100 days of age. Only two (one male and one female) cloth-surrogate-raised monkeys were observed to show pelvic thrusting to the surrogate, and this occurred initially at approximately 100 days of age. Frequency of this sexual play was much higher toward real mothers than toward surrogates. In both situations maximal frequency occurred at about five months and then declined, apparently being superseded by thrusting directed toward other infants.

Surrogate babies and mothered babies showed no significant differences in first-observed, infant-directed thrusting, but the actual mean score of the surrogate group was lower. The frequency of sexual play was higher for the real-mothered babies than for the surrogate babies. Finally, seven of eight mother-raised monkeys showed appropriate adult-form sex behaviors during the first 18 months, including ankle clasp by the males, whereas adult-oriented sex behavior was not observed in the cloth-surrogate-raised babies.

There is every reason to believe that normal mothering facilitates the development of heterosexual behavior in rhesus monkeys. This may be in part the result of direct contacts with the mother growing out of the intimate bonds between mother and child. One must not, however, underestimate the importance of the role which the real mother apparently plays, indirect though it is, in stimulating the infants to associate with other infants. This is accomplished from the third month on by discouraging the infant from constant clinging as it matures.

From time to time the mother restrains the infant's approaches or cuffs it if it nips her or pulls her hair. The chastised infant seeks the companionship of other babies until the storm subsides—the other mothers by this time generally reject all but their own babies—and in the infant-infant interchanges strong affectional bonds develop along with behaviors, sexual and nonsexual, appropriate to the sexes.

In the present study, as in all ordinary human situations, there is confounding in the roles played by the mother-infant affectional systems and the infant-infant and peer-peer affectional systems in determining later behavior. We expect to resolve this in part by raising two groups of monkey babies with real mothers, but denying them any opportunity to interact with other infants for six months in the one group and 12 months in the other before subjecting them to social testing.

Some information is supplied by another experiment involving eight rhesus babies raised on cloth surrogate mothers, but tested 20 minutes a day in the playroom, which is a more stimulating environment than that afforded by the relatively cramped and bare confines of the play compartments of the playpen situation. These surrogate-mothered babies showed excellent and appropriately timed play behaviors and very early came to assume both sexual and nonsexual behaviors appropriate to males and females. The males threatened, the females did not; the males initiated rough-and-tumble play, but not the females. Males chased males and males chased females, but females practically never chased males and seldom chased females. By a year of age considerable appropriate male and female sex behavior had occurred, and full and complete copulation, other than insemination, was repeatedly observed in the two males and two females on which observations were continued during the second year of life.

It is obvious that we must not underestimate the importance and role of the infant-infant affectional system as a determiner of adolescent and adult adjustments. It is more than possible that this system is essential if the animal is to respond positively to sheer physical contact with a peer, and it is through the operation of this system, probably both in monkey and man, that sexual roles become identified and, usually, acceptable.

The role of the mother in the formation of the adult personality is obviously important, but the exact mechanics are open for experimentation. The most tender and intimate associations occur at a stage in which the monkey infant and human infant can to a considerable extent be molded. Monkey and human mother both have the obligation of gradually dissolving the intense physical bonds which characterize the early mother-child relationship. For the monkey mother it is easy and natural—when the infant becomes mature enough and strong enough to become bothersome, she rejects or punishes it and the baby retreats for a time. Subsequently, she welcomes the baby back. Independence is gradually established. For the human mother, with her more complicated motivational systems and her complex culture, it may be difficult to achieve this gradual separation. The overprotective mother is a well-known clinical extreme in the human problem of weaning the infant and child emotionally. Probably the surrogate monkey mother is a parallel of the overprotective human mother, failing usually to equal the normal mother in rearing socially and sexually adjusted monkeys because, at least in part, she is ever available to provide comfort and security. She never discourages contact and thereby never encourages independence in her infant and affectional relationships with other infants and children. The normal state of complete dependency necessary in early infancy is prolonged until it hinders normal personal-social development.

As we have already pointed out, four of our laboratory-raised females never had real mothers of their own, one being raised in a bare wire cage and three with cloth surrogates. The first week after the birth of the baby to the wire-cage-raised female, the mother sat fixedly at one side of the cage staring into space, almost unaware of her infant or of human beings, even when they barked at and threatened the baby. There was no sign of maternal responses, and when the infant approached and attempted contact, the mother rebuffed it, often with vigor, as shown in Figure 3.

Figure 3.

The next two unmothered mothers constantly rebuffed the approaches of their infants, but, in addition, frequently engaged in cruel and unprovoked attacks. They struck and beat their babies, mouthed them roughly, and pushed their faces into the wire-mesh floor. These attacks seemed to be exaggerated in the presence of human beings, and for this reason all formal testing was abandoned for three days for the third unmothered mother because we feared for the life of the infant.

Figure 4.

The fourth unmothered mother ignored and rejected her infant but did not exhibit excessive cruelty.

In strong contrast to the frailty of the maternal affectional system was the vigor and persistence of the infants' bondage to the mother—time after time, hour after hour, the infants returned, contacted, and clasped the mother in spite of being hit, kicked, and scraped unceremoniously off the mother's body, as shown in Figure 4. The physical punishment which these infants took or sought for the privilege of brief contact even to the back or side of the mother's body testified to the fact that, even in infants, attachment to the mother may be prepotent over pain and suffering. One could not help but be reminded of children, removed from indifferent or cruel, indigent, and alcoholic parents, whose primary insistent wish is to return home.

The degree to which monkey data are generalizable to the human being will remain an unsolved dilemma. Nevertheless, we are so struck by the many apparent analogies that we are tempted to say the monkey experiments give us faith in the human clinical observations.

SUMMARY

Infant rhesus monkeys have been reared starting on the first day of life in a variety of situations, including total isolation; partial isolation, either in individual bare wire cages in a colony room for two years or longer, or in individual wire cages with access to one or two mother surrogates for at least the first six months; and in situations with real or surrogate mothers plus contact with other infants for the first year or two of life.

Total isolation for two years resulted in failure to display social or sexual behavior in the next two years, spent in a joint living cage. Results on six months of such isolation are still being gathered and suggest severe, but not complete, social deficits. Only mild effects have been observed thus far in monkeys isolated through the first 80 days of life.

Partial isolation has produced behavioral aberrations in many monkeys and sexual inadequacy in all males and in all but one female. Four females were impregnated, in spite of inadequate posturing, and proved to be completely inadequate mothers.

Infants raised by live mothers were more advanced in social and sexual behavior than infants raised by surrogate mothers in a controlled playpen situation. The mother's role is not entirely clear, however, because in a more stimulating playroom situation, surrogate-mothered babies have shown normal social and sexual behavior.

Over all, it appears that the longer and the more complete the social deprivation, the more devastating are the behavioral effects. Further research is needed to evaluate the relative contributions of live mothers and infant companions to later adjustment.

WILLIAM C. YOUNG, ROBERT W. GOY, AND
CHARLES H. PHOENIX *

9

HORMONES AND SEXUAL
BEHAVIOR

Research on the relationships between the hormones and sexual behavior has not been pursued with the vigor justified by the biological, medical, and sociological importance of the subject. Explanation may lie in the stigma any activity associated with sexual behavior has long borne. In our experience, restraint has been requested in the use of the word *sex* in institutional records and in the title of research proposals. We vividly recollect that the propriety of presenting certain data at scientific meetings and seminars was questioned. Counteracting this deterrent is the stimulation which has come from colleagues in many disciplines to whom we have appealed for help, and the satisfaction we have felt in seeing a picture emerge as the pieces of the puzzle have been studied and fitted together.

---

* The authors are members of the scientific staff of the Oregon Regional Primate Research Center in Reproductive Physiology and Behavior, Beaverton.

RELATIONSHIPS IN THE ADULT

Causal connections between gonadal hormones and the development of the capacity of infrahuman vertebrates to display sexual behavior have long been assumed, although the existence of such relationships in man is questioned (1–3). Doubt has also been expressed that a specific relationship exists between any one hormone (or class of hormones) and the behavior it facilitates in adults in general, from fish to man (4–6).

A number of explanations may be given for the uncertainty which exists. Human sexual activity is influenced by many psychologic factors, the social level, cultural background, and tradition. The many reports are not completely trustworthy. Physiological correlates with individual behavior are largely nonexistent, and controlled study in man as we know it in laboratory animals is impossible. In our opinion the many differences in behavior which in the growing child and adult are socially rather than hormonally determined have obscured the possible role of the hormones in maintaining the strength of the sexual drive. Even in lower mammals the same quantity of hormone elicits almost as many modes of response as there are individuals. This fact may have contributed to the doubt, to which we have alluded, that there is any great degree of hormonal specificity. In the human female, sexual responsiveness does not have the sharp relationship to folliculogenesis and to the functioning of the corpus luteum in the ovary that it does in most lower mammals (7). The degree to which this evolutionary change within the primates has been accompanied by an emancipation from the effects of hormonal action is not known.

The need for testicular androgen in the maintenance of sexual vigor in the male has been questioned by some students of the problem. In man (5, 8), the dog (9), the domestic cat (10), fishes (6), and birds (11), there is, in males, a persistence of sexual activity for some weeks or months after castration which has not been explained satisfactorily; a corresponding persistence is encountered rarely if at all in females below the primates. The restoration of sexual vigor by replacement therapy also requires weeks in the male and only hours or days in the female. The longer time lapse which occurs, regardless of the direction of hormonal change, suggests that the manner of hormonal action in the male is greatly different from that in the female rather than that the strength of sexual behavior is independent of the presence of testicular androgen.

Finally, in this brief consideration of the subject, there are the important studies of deviant sexual types by Hampson and Hampson (1), Money (2), and the recent report by Völkel (3). The data these clinical investigators collected led them to conclude that the establishment of gender role or psychologic sex can be independent of chromosomal sex, gonadal sex, hormonal sex, internal reproductive structures, and external genital morphology. They relate the process rather to "the many experiences of growing up, including those experiences dictated by his or her own bodily equipment" (1).

The interest of one of us (W.C.Y.) in the relationship of the hormones to sexual behavior goes back to an observation made during his graduate years at the University of Chicago when he was looking for signs that would be useful in the identification of female guinea pigs in heat. No active interest was taken, however, until more than 6 years later. During a lull at Brown University, Young, Hugh I. Myers, and Edward W. Dempsey, while waiting for what turned out to be the disapproval of an application for a small amount of money for work on the function of the epididymis, fell into a discussion of the abrupt and dramatic change that occurs in the behavior of the female guinea pig when she comes into heat. They wondered whether this change is associated with any structural change in the ovaries. Continuous day and night observation of the laboratory animals for several months was rewarded by the information Young and his co-workers were seeking. The beginning of heat was found to coincide closely with the beginning of the preovulatory growth phase of the Graafian follicle (12); it could be that the three investigators, none of whom had any training in psychology, had stumbled on the only spontaneously occurring macroscopic structural change associated with the alteration of a behavioral state in a mammal.

The reports that ovariectomized mice, rats, rabbits, and

dogs copulated after the injection of follicular fluid or of the estrogens that were available at that time suggested that the same behavior would occur in the guinea pig. To the surprise of Young and his associates, irregular results were obtained. These led to the conclusion that a second substance must participate. With the help of Roy Hertz, who worked with the group that year, Dempsey took his cue as to the nature of this substance from the demonstration that the preovulatory growth phase in anestrous cats is stimulated by hypophyseal luteinizing hormone (13). Tests soon revealed that this gonadotrophin does not produce heat directly; they suggested that, by stimulating preovulatory swelling, ovulation, and production of progesterone, luteinizing hormone leads indirectly to the display of estrous behavior by animals previously injected with an estrogen (14). The progesterone as it turned out, was the second participating substance. Its synergistic action in combination with estrogens to bring latent mating behavior to expression has since been demonstrated in an impressive number of mammalian species (see 7). Astwood (15) showed later that the hypophyseal gonadotrophin responsible for the production of progesterone is luteotrophin rather than luteinizing hormone.

IMPORTANCE OF SOMA

The familiarity obtained with the behavior of the female guinea pig and later with that of the rat and male guinea pig revealed (i) that in repeated tests individual differences in behavior were remarkably consistent and reliable (16, 17); (ii) that in the female these differences, except perhaps for the male-like mounting behavior, are not related to the number of rupturing Graafian follicles (18, 19); and (iii) that in neither sex are the differences in the vigor of the behavior related to the quantity of administered hormones, provided of course a threshold has been exceeded (17, 20). These findings led to the realization that the nature of the latent behavior brought to expression by gonadal hormones depends largely on the character of the soma or substrate on which the hormones act (19). The substrate was assumed to be neural (9). Unknown to Young and his co-workers until 15 or 20 years later, Goodale

(21) in 1918 had been impressed by the failure of ovaries implanted into capons to feminize their behavior and had written, "the character of sexual reactions seems to depend upon the substratum, while the gonad merely determines that it shall be given expression."

FACTORS INFLUENCING CHARACTER OF SOMA

It follows from this principle that an investigator trying to account for the behavioral differences between individuals, instead of looking to the gonadal hormones, would do better to look to the factors which influence the character of the tissues on which these hormones act. The age of the animal was one of the first factors investigated, and data indicating that age is significant were obtained immediately. Responsiveness or reactivity of the tissues to injected gonadal hormones is lacking during early infancy and increases gradually to the level observed in the adult (22, 23).

The possibility of further changes as aging progresses has not been investigated. The thyroid was thought of as a factor influencing responsiveness, and Young and his coworkers found that female guinea pigs surgically thyroidectomized and given I^{131}, to suppress any accessory thyroid activity, ovariectomized, and injected with estradiol and progesterone were less responsive to the latter substances than control females (24). The many reports of the effects of thyroid hormone on the vigor of sexual behavior in the male are so contradictory (7) that prediction of the relation of this hormone to the animal's responsiveness to androgens, before adequately designed experiments have been carried out, would be unwise.

The belief that the genetic background is an influential determinant of the character of the soma was soon confirmed. Intact male and female guinea pigs of the highly inbred strains 2 and 13 exhibit significant differences in their behavior. The differences are displayed consistently after gonadectomy and injection of the same amounts of the appropriate hormones (20, 23, 25). The hereditary basis of sexual behavior was studied. For both male and female behavior a high degree of heritability was demonstrated. The inheritance is autosomal, of the sex-limited or sex-influenced type, and appears to be polygenic for most of the behavioral characteristics studied. Sexual behavior is not inherited as a unitary trait, and the elements composing the patterns of behavior show a surprising degree of independence of one another. In the male, phenotypic dominance of strain 13 was found for specific behavioral characteristics—for example, frequency of mounting. With respect to other characteristics, such as latency to ejaculation, strain 2 was dominant (26). In the female, the characteristics of frequent male-like mounting, vigorous lordosis, and responsiveness to injected estrogen appeared to have independent modes of inheritance and separate genetic bases (27).

Attention was drawn to the possibility that experiential or psychologic factors might have a role in the determination of the character of the soma by two young psychologists in the laboratory, Elliott S. Valenstein and Walter Riss, who could not accept the view that inheritance was accounting for the entire action. Again, the hunch was a good one. In a relatively short time after they directed their attention to the behavior of guinea pig males raised in isolation from the day of birth, except for association with the mother, the necessity of contact with other animals for the maturation of normal patterns of sexual behavior was demonstrated (28). These males were sexually aroused to the same degree as normal males and attempted to mount frequently. However, the males that had been raised in isolation displayed an inability to properly mount and clasp a female. Presumably as a result of this inability, intromission was rarely achieved. These behavioral deficiencies characteristic of males reared in isolation were not overcome by injections of testosterone propionate and therefore cannot be attributed to a hormonal deficiency. The effect of isolation on maturation of the behavior of the female is less pronounced, except, interestingly, that isolation has an inhibiting effect on the male-like mounting behavior displayed so commonly by the female guinea pig (29). The guinea pig is not alone in needing contact with other animals for the maturation of normal behavior. This need has been demonstrated many times in species as widely separated phylogenetically as ring doves, domestic turkeys, rats, cats, rhesus monkeys, chimpanzees, and man (10, 30).

SPECIAL INFLUENCE OF EARLY HORMONAL FACTORS

Up to this point nothing in the work with young or adult animals had suggested that gonadal hormones serve to organize the tissues mediating sexual behavior in the sense of differentiation, as experimental embryologists use the word. Conceivably the action is organizational before birth or before sexual maturation, and activational in the adult.

We were aware that numerous investigators have obtained a full functional sex reversal (including breeding) in fishes and amphibians after administering heterotypical hormones during the embryonic and larval stages [see 31 for a few of the many reports reviewed by Young (32)]. More important for our thought was the statement by Dantchakoff (33) that female guinea pigs given testosterone prenatally had ovaries and two sets of duct systems. Oviducts, uterus, and vagina existed along with epididymides, ducti deferentes, seminal vesicles, prostate, Cowper's glands, and a penis, all differentiated and developed to varying degrees. An inverse relationship was found between penile structure and the degree of vaginal development. After injections of testosterone, masculine behavior was displayed. A repetition of Dantchakoff's experiment was dictated by the circumstance that no controls seem to have been used in her studies of this species, in which most normal females display male-like mounting as a part of the estrous reactions. Once a satisfactory method of administering the hormone had been developed by Myron D. Tedford, whose interest was mainly in the structural changes, pseudohermaphroditic females were produced routinely. The genital tracts were similar to those described by Dantchakoff, although probably encompassing a larger range of variations in structure. A marked display of masculine behavior was seen, as well as a lowered capacity to display feminine behavior (34)—an effect not observed by the earlier workers. Loss of the ability to come into heat was greatest when androgen treatment was started on day 30 of the 67- to 71-day gestation period, regardless of the duration of treatment and the total amount of androgen (35) (Table 1).

TABLE 1   LOSS OF THE ABILITY OF FEMALE GUINEA PIGS TO COME INTO HEAT RELATIVE TO THE AMOUNT OF ANDROGEN (TESTOSTERONE PROPIONATE) INJECTED IN THE PRENATAL PERIOD AND TO THE LENGTH OF THE PERIOD OF TREATMENT

Period of prenatal injection of androgen (days)	Total amount of androgen injected (mg)	Percentage failing to come into heat
15 to 30	40	0
15 to 40	50	12
15 to 45	55	36
15 to 60 +	70 +	27
20 to 65	70	45
25 to 40	40	23
30 to 45	40	67
30 to 55 or 65	50 or 60	92 or 91
35 to 65	55	60
40 to 65	50	33
50 to 65	40	0

For us, these results produced an exciting moment. It was clear, first, that the gonadal hormones, or at least testicular androgens, have a dual role in the control of sexual behavior in the guinea pig. During the fetal period the hormones have an organizing action on the neural tissues destined to mediate mating behavior after the attainment of adulthood; during adulthood their role is one of activation. In other words, during fetal morphogenesis androgens exert a fundamental influence on the organization of the soma, determining whether the sexual reactions brought to expression in the adult will be masculine or feminine in character.

Second, it was clear that the rules of hormonal action are identical with those shown by the experimental embryologists to be applicable to the genital tracts (36). During the fetal period the gonadal hormones influence the direction of differentiation. During adulthood they stimulate functioning, be it contraction of smooth muscle fiber, secretion of epithelial cells, or endometrial sensitization for implantation.

The comparison can be extended. Evidence has been presented by experimental embryologists that, as the male develops, fetal testicular hormone is responsible for differentiation of the Wolffian duct system (precursor of the male genital tract) and suppression of the Müllerian duct system (precursor of the female genital tract). In the female and in the castrated fetal male, in both of which testicular androgen is absent, there is development of the Müllerian duct system and regression of the Wolffian duct system. In our experiments the administration of an androgen to developing female fetuses was followed by the production of individuals in which there had been a stimulating action on the tissues (presumably neural) having the potential capacity for mediating masculine behavior, and a suppressing action on the tissues destined ordinarily to mediate feminine behavior.

In order to complete the analogy it was necessary to demonstrate that genotypic males castrated before the end of the period in which the organizing action of the fetal testicular hormone ordinarily occurs would display feminine behavior as adults. For us, such an operation on the young fetal guinea pig was not feasible. The best available evidence from tests of fertility and mating behavior indicated that this organizational period in the rat, a species with a short period of gestation, is postnatal (37) rather than prenatal, and that it ends at approximately the 10th day after birth. If the analogy could be extended, male rats castrated during this short period after birth should display feminine behavior, or at least elements of feminine behavior, when injected with estrogen and progesterone as adults.

An experiment designed to test this hypothesis has just been completed by Kenneth L. Grady, a graduate student. Male rats were castrated at 1, 5, 10, 20, 30, 50, and 90 days of age, and as a criterion, females were ovariectomized at 90 days. When they were 120 days old, and from then on, all animals were tested, after injections of estradiol and progesterone, for the display of feminine behavior in response to mounting by intact males. As we had expected, the experimental males displayed feminine behavior. Those castrated on day 1 or day 5 displayed significantly more receptive behavior than those castrated as late as day 10. Castration later than day 10 did not promote the retention or development of female behavioral characteristics (38) (see Table 2).

TABLE 2   MEAN COPULATORY QUOTIENTS (LORDOSIS/MOUNTS) FOR RATS GONADECTOMIZED AT DIFFERENT AGES AND TESTED AFTER INJECTION OF ESTRADIOL AND PROGESTERONE AT 120 DAYS

Day of gonadectomy	Quotient
Females	
90	0.619
Males	
1	0.436
5	.218
10	.014
20	.029
30	.042
50	.026
90	.019

Tests of masculine behavior in male rats castrated soon after birth and tested as adults are currently in progress. When these tests are completed the model established by the experimental embryologists will have been duplicated for behavior. The results may be anticipated from an early study in which male rats castrated on day 1 exhibited a marked deficiency in copulatory ability as compared with those castrated on day 21 or later (39). If this proves to be a representative finding, our work on the two sexes will have produced complementary pictures of the organizational influences of androgen. On the one hand, females treated with androgen during the appropriate period show a regression or inhibition of feminine behavior and an accentuation of masculine behavioral traits. Males deprived of the principal source of endogenous andro- gen during a comparable period show accentuated feminine behavior and the absence of, or a greatly diminished capacity for, masculine behavior.

EXTENSION TO SEX-RELATED BEHAVIOR

When Phoenix, Goy, Gerall, and Young (34) were sum- marizing their data on the behavior of the female pseudo- hermaphroditic guinea pigs, they suggested that the organizing or sex-differentiating action of fetal gonadal substances may affect behavior beyond that which is primarily sexual in the sense of being directed solely toward the attainment of sexual aims. The rhesus monkey seemed better suited than the guinea pig or rat for a test of this hypothesis, so we proceeded accord- ingly.

Although an androgen treatment entirely compatible with the maintenance of pregnancy has not been worked out, we have succeeded in producing three female pseudohermaph- roditic subjects with conspicuous genital alterations (Fig. 1). Two have been studied in considerable detail. We based our study of the early social patterns displayed by these individuals on the model established by Leonard Rosenblum during his graduate training at the University of Wisconsin. Accordingly, the pseudohermaphroditic females were allowed unrestricted social interaction with two untreated females for 20 minutes per day, 5 days per week, in a specially designed play room.

The results from 90 such observational sessions, covering the second through the fifth months of life, have been analyzed recently. A number of social behaviors, known to be sexually dimorphic and without any immediate instrumentality relative to mating, appear to have been influenced in the masculine direction by our prenatal treatments with androgen. The social behavior of the untreated females did not differ importantly from that described for normal females by Rosenblum, but the behavior of the treated females much more closely re- sembled his description of that of males. The pseudohermaph- roditic females threatened, initiated play, and engaged in rough-and-tumble play patterns more frequently than the con-

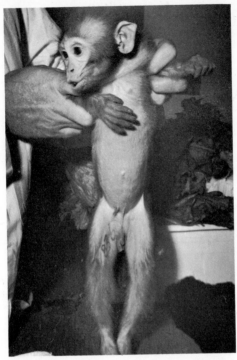

Figure 1. Female pseudohermaphrodite produced by injecting testosterone propionate into the mother during pregnancy. The treatment involved injection of 25 mg daily from post-coital day 40 through day 50; 20 mg from day 51 through day 70; and 10 mg from day 71 through day 90. There were no injections during the balance of the 166-day period of gestation. A prominent and well-formed phallus is visible to the right of the empty scrotal fold. The surgical scar in the right inguinal region resulted from a laparotomy which showed that there was no testis.

trols (Figs. 2–4). Like the males studied by Rosenblum, these pseudohermaphrodites also withdrew less often from the initiations, threats, and approaches of other subjects.

Analysis of the sexual behavior displayed by these pseudohermaphroditic females, although far from complete, already shows that it is not only in their patterns of withdrawing, playing, and threatening that they display a bias

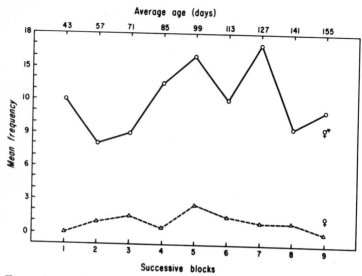

Figure 2. Display of facial threat by female pseudohermaphroditic (solid line) and normal female (broken line) monkeys plotted relative to age. The abscissa is scaled in successive blocks of five trials.

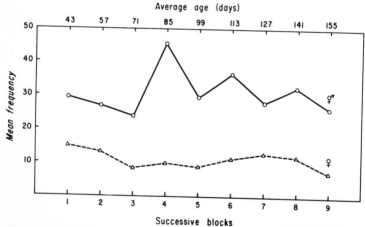

Figure 3. Invitation to play by female pseudohermaphroditic (solid line) and normal female (broken line) monkeys, plotted relative to age. The abscissa is scaled in successive blocks of five trials.

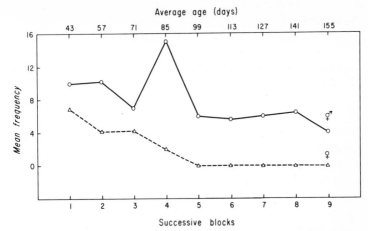

Figure 4. Rough-and-tumble play by female pseudohermaphroditic (solid line) and normal female (broken line) monkeys, plotted relative to age. The abscissa is scaled in successive blocks of five trials.

toward masculinity. In special tests with pairs of females, one pseudohermaphroditic and one normal, the pseudohermaphrodites consistently displayed more frequent attempts to mount, regardless of whether the normal female was brought to the hermaphroditic female's cage or vice versa. Their attempts to mount, while infantile and poorly oriented, are beginning to be integrated with pelvic thrusting and even, on a few occasions, phallic erection.

Our work with the primates has not progressed to a point where it may be considered definitive, partly because of the limited duration of the study and partly because of the very small number of subjects. We nevertheless consider the results to be highly encouraging and supportive of the general conclusions developed in our more extensive studies with the infraprimate mammals, concerning the action of the gonadal hormones.

IMPLICATIONS

Implied in the present discussion of data bearing on the organizing action of androgen on the neural tissues destined to mediate sexual behavior is the view that a part or parts of the central nervous system are masculine or feminine, depending on the sex of the individual. This concept is not new; it has been developing over the years in the writings of investigators whose approach has been entirely different from ours (4, 40). What we have found adds support to this view and suggests something of the way in which masculinity or femininity is conferred on the nervous system.

An additional thought merits attention. It is that the principles of hormonal action in effecting this sexual differentiation of the developing brain provide a model to which we may look for a reexamination of the psychosexual incongruities discussed by Hampson and Hampson (1) and by Money (2) in their reviews and in their many articles published since the middle 1950's. We accept and, in our own work with lower mammals, have documented the importance of the subject's experience. However, explanation of the cases these investigators present need not lead to a rejection of the concept of a predetermined psychosexuality for the concept of a psychologic sexual neutrality at birth. If the endocrinology of the differentiation of the capacity to display masculine and feminine sexual behavior as we have worked it out for the guinea pig and the rat is applicable to man, the incongruities in the patients these workers examined can be explained without postulating a psychosexual neutrality at birth and attributing the gender role and sexual orientation solely to the individual's life experiences while growing up. In view of what we have learned an endocrinological basis which is consistent with the concept of psychologic bisexuality exists for the interpretation of most if not all of the cases they report. This is true of their hermaphrodites with ambiguous or masculinized external genitals and with a female sex chromatin pattern (comparable with our female pseudohermaphrodites); of the cryptorchid hermaphrodites with a male sex chromatin pattern, in which testicular function was clearly subnormal; of the simulant females with a male sex chromatin pattern but with the as yet unexplained feminizing testes; and of the "females" born with gonadal dysgenesis and an XO or XY chromosome pattern (Turner's syndrome). The large group of hyperadrenocortical patients with the female sex chromosome pattern probably would fit into this picture were the circumstances such that more information about the parameters of the excessive androgen production could have been obtained.

We realize as we venture into a clinical area that a question exists regarding the extent to which what we have found in the guinea pig, rat, and monkey is applicable to man. We call attention, however, to an interesting similarity revealed by Milton Diamond during his graduate work at the University of Kansas. After noting that testosterone does not induce masculinization of the adult female guinea pig while it is pregnant, he examined the clinical literature and found an apparent comparable lack of masculinization in pregnant human beings: 27 of 31 women who received androgenic hormones or gestagens in quantities sufficient to masculinize the female fetuses were not themselves virilized (41).

DIRECTION OF FUTURE RESEARCH

As we have proceeded with our analysis of the relationships of the hormones to sexual behavior and, more recently, to sex-related behavior, we have always been aware that many questions remain to be answered. At the same time a picture is emerging, and, with good fortune in the selection of materials and techniques, much more of it will be revealed in the future.

Without discounting the influence of psychologic factors, which we know is great, or the need for carefully recorded observations of behavior, we expect that, increasingly, the materials and techniques used will be those of the neurologist and the biochemist. The directions many neurologists are taking are indicated by the various reports of efforts to locate the neurological sites of hormonal action and define the pathways of stimuli for the many responses that are given (see 42).

Few biochemists have been attracted to the problem, but it is they who must clarify the mechanisms of hormonal action in organizing the tissues of the central nervous system during development and in bringing behavior to expression in the adult. They may be helped in such a search by the circumstance that cellular elements in the genital tracts, which differentiate and are activated under the influence of these same hormones, are at present more accessible for histophysiological study than those in tissues of the central nervous system. It is to be hoped that clues will come from the work of the many investigators whose studies are described in recent reviews (43).

The need for studies of sexual behavior in man is great. Methods for collecting trustworthy, meaningful data and means of ascertaining whether the many behavioral states are associated with hormonal action in the developing fetus and in the adult should be worked out. The possibility that such relationships exist and that typical and deviant behaviors have a physiologic as well as a psychologic basis may no longer be excluded.

SUMMARY

From an attempt made 30 years ago to attain a limited objective, we have proceeded with what turned out to be a long-term investigation. Evidence has accumulated indicating that the gonadal hormones have a broad role in the determination of behavior. We have long known that they act to bring sexual behavior to expression, certainly in adult vertebrates below man. We now know, in addition, that during a period of organization and differentiation which is prenatal in the guinea pig and monkey and postnatal in the rat, the hormones act according to principles which appear to be identical with those operative during the differentiation of the genital tracts, and they effect a corresponding differentiation or organization of neural tissues.

The data thus far accumulated from a study of the behavior of two female pseudohermaphroditic monkeys suggest that this early hormonal action is also responsible for the establishment of much of the sex-related behavior which is a part of the masculinity or femininity of an individual but which is not related directly to the reproductive processes.

REFERENCES AND NOTES

1. J. L. HAMPSON and J. G. HAMPSON, in *Sex and Internal Secretions,* W. C. Young, Ed. (Williams and Wilkins, Baltimore, ed. 3, 1961), p. 1401.

2. J. MONEY, *ibid.*, p. 1383.

3. H. VON VÖLKEL, *Psychiat. Neurol. 145*, 257 (1963).

4. J. T. EAYRS, *Ciba Found. Colloq. Endocrinol. 3*, 18 (1952).

5. A. C. KINSEY, W. B. POMEROY, C. E. MARTIN, P. H. GEBHARD, *Sexual Behavior in the Human Female* (Saunders, Philadelphia, 1953).

6. L. R. ARONSON, in *The Physiology of Fishes*, M. E. Brown, Ed. (Academic Press, New York, 1957), p. 272.

7. W. C. YOUNG, in *Sex and Internal Secretions*, W. C. Young, Ed. (Williams and Wilkins, Baltimore, 1961), p. 1173.

8. F. A. BEACH, *Hormones and Behavior* (Hoeber, New York, 1948); J. BREMER, *Asexualization, a Follow-up Study of 244 Cases* (Macmillan, New York, 1959).

9. F. A. BEACH, *Ciba Found. Colloq. Endocrinol. 3*, 3 (1952).

10. J. S. ROSENBLATT and L. R. ARONSON, *Behaviour 12*, 285 (1958).

11. J. BENOIT, *Arch. Zool. Exptl. Gen. 69*, 217 (1929); C. R. CARPENTER, *J. Comp. Psychol. 16*, 25, 59 (1933); H. M. SCOTT and L. F. PAYNE, *J. Exptl. Zool. 69*, 123 (1934); F. CARIDROIT, in *Nouveau Traité de Physiologie*, G. Duma, Ed. (Alcan, Paris, 1946), vol. 3, bk. 2, p. 109.

12. H. I. MYERS, W. C. YOUNG, E. W. DEMPSEY, *Anat. Rec. 65*, 381 (1936).

13. M. A. FOSTER and F. L. HISAW, *ibid. 62*, 75 (1935).

14. E. W. DEMPSEY, R. HERTZ, W. C. YOUNG, *Am. J. Physiol. 116*, 201 (1936).

15. E. B. ASTWOOD, *Endocrinology 28*, 309 (1951)

16. W. C. YOUNG, E. W. DEMPSEY, C. W. HAGQUIST, J. L. BOLING, *J. Comp. Psychol. 27*, 49 (1939); R. J. BLANDAU, J. L. BOLING, W. C. YOUNG, *Anat. Rec. 79*, 453 (1941); W. C. YOUNG and W. R. FISH, *Endocrinology 36*, 181 (1945); W. C. YOUNG, in *Roots of Behavior, Genetics, Instinct, and Socialization in Animal Behavior*, E. L. Bliss, Ed. (Hoeber-Harper, New York, 1962), p. 115.

17. J. A. GRUNT and W. C. YOUNG, *Endocrinology 51*, 237 (1952).

18. W. C. YOUNG, H. I. MYERS, E. W. DEMPSEY, *Am. J. Physiol. 105*, 393 (1933).

19. W. C. YOUNG, E. W. DEMPSEY, H. I. MYERS, C. W. HAGQUIST, *Am. J. Anat. 63*, 457 (1938).

20. R. W. GOY and W. C. YOUNG, *Behaviour 10*, 340 (1957).

21. H. D. GOODALE, *Genetics 3*, 276 (1918).

22. J. G. WILSON and W. C. YOUNG, *Endocrinology 29*, 779 (1941).

23. W. RISS, E. S. VALENSTEIN, J. SINKS, W. C. YOUNG, *ibid. 57*, 139 (1955).

24. R. M. HOAR, R. W. GOY, W. C. YOUNG, *ibid. 60*, 337 (1957).

25. E. S. VALENSTEIN, W. RISS, W. C. YOUNG, *J. Comp. Physiol. Psychol. 47*, 162 (1954).

26. J. S. JAKWAY, *Animal Behaviour 7*, 150 (1959).

27. R. W. GOY and J. S. JAKWAY, *ibid.*, p. 142.

28. E. S. VALENSTEIN, W. RISS, W. C. YOUNG, *J. Comp. Physiol. Psychol. 48*, 397 (1955); E. S. VALENSTEIN and W. C. YOUNG, *Endocrinology 56*, 173 (1955); E. S. VALENSTEIN and R. W. GOY, *J. Comp. Physiol. Psychol. 50*, 115 (1957).

29. R. W. GOY and W. C. YOUNG, *Psychosom. Med. 19*, 144 (1957).

30. H. F. HARLOW and M. K. HARLOW, *Sci. Am. 207*, 136 (1962); W. CRAIG, *J. Animal Behavior 4*, 121 (1914); M. W. SCHEIN and E. B. HALE, *Animal Behaviour 7*, 189 (1959); F. A. BEACH, *J. Genet. Psychol. 60*, 121 (1942); G. ZIMBARDO, *J. Comp. Physiol. Psychol. 51*, 764 (1958); J. S. ROSENBLATT and L. R. ARONSON, *Animal Behaviour 6*, 171 (1958); H. W. NISSEN, unpublished manuscript (available from the University of Kansas Library); J. BOWLBY, *Bull. World Health Organ. 3*, 355 (1951).

31. L. GALLIEN, *Bull. Biol. France Belgique 78*, 257 (1944); ———, in *Progress in Comparative Endocrinology*, K. Take-waki, Ed. (Academic Press, New York, 1962), p. 346; R. R. HUMPHREY, *Am. J. Anat. 76*, 33 (1945); W. LASKOWSKI, *Arch. Entwicklungsmech. Organ. 146*, 137 (1953); T. O. YAMAMOTO, *J. Exptl. Zool. 123*, 571 (1953); ———, *ibid. 141*, 133 (1959); C. Y. CHANG and E. WITSCHI, *Proc. Soc. Exptl. Biol. Med. 89*, 150 (1955).

32. W. C. YOUNG, in *Comparative Biochemistry*, Vol. 7. M. Florkin and H. Mason, Eds. (Academic Press, New York, 1964), pp. 203–251.

33. V. DANTCHAKOFF, *Compt. Rend. 206*, 945 (1938); ———, *Compt. Rend. Soc. Biol. 127*, 1255 (1938); V. DANTSCHAKOFF, *Biol. Zentr. 58*, 302 (1938).

34. C. H. PHOENIX, R. W. GOY, A. A. GERALL, W. C. YOUNG, *Endocrinology 65*, 369 (1959).

35. R. W. GOY, W. E. BRIDSON, W. C. YOUNG, *J. Comp. Physiol. Psychol.*, in press.

36. R. K. BURNS, *Surv. Biol. Progr. 1*, 233 (1949); ———, in *Sex and Internal Secretions*, W. C. Young, Ed. (Williams and Wilkins, Baltimore, ed. 3, 1961), p. 76; A. JOST, *Arch. Anat. Microscop. Morphol. Exptl. 36*, 151, 242, 271 (1947); ———, *Recent Progr. Hormone Res. 8*, 379 (1953); ———, in *Conference on Gestation: Transactions of the 3rd and 4th Conferences*, C. A. Villee, Ed. (Josiah Macy Jr. Foundation, New York, 1957), p. 129; L. J. WELLS, M. W. CAVANAUGH, E. L. MAXWELL, *Anat. Rec. 118*, 109 (1954); D. PRICE, E. ORTIZ,

R. Pannabecker, *Proc. Intern. Congr. Cell Biol., 10th, Paris* (1960), p. 158.

37. C. A. Barraclough, *Endocrinology 68*, 62 (1961); R. W. Goy, C. H. Phoenix, W. C. Young, *Anat. Rec. 142*, 307 (1962).

38. K. L. Grady and C. H. Phoenix, *Am. Zool., 3*, 482 (1963).

39. F. A. Beach and A. M. Holz, *J. Exptl. Zool. 101*, 91 (1946).

40. C. A. Pfeiffer, *Am. J. Anat. 58*, 195 (1936); J. W. Everett, C. H. Sawyer, J. E. Markee, *Endocrinology 44*, 234 (1949); G. W. Harris, *Neural Control of the Pituitary Gland* (Arnold, London, 1955); ———, in *Frontiers in Brain Research*, J. D. French, Ed. (Columbia Univ. Press, New York, 1962), p. 191; ———, *J. Reprod. Fertility 5*, 299 (1963); G. W. Harris and S. Levine, *J. Physiol. London 163*, 42 (1962).

41. M. Diamond and W. C. Young, *Endocrinology 72*, 429 (1963).

42. J. L. Green, C. D. Clemente, J. de Groot, *J. Comp. Neurol. 108*, 505 (1957); G. W. Harris, R. P. Michael, P. P. Scott, in *Ciba Foundation Symposium on the Neurological Basis of Behaviour*, G. E. W. Wolstenholme and C. M. O. O'Connor, Eds. (Little, Brown, Boston, 1958), p. 236; M. Kawakami and C. H. Sawyer, *Endocrinology 65*, 652 (1959); ———, *ibid.*, p. 631; C. H. Sawyer and M. Kawakami, *ibid.*, p. 622; R. D. Lisk, *J. Exptl. Zool. 145*, 197 (1960); R. D. Lisk and M. Newlon, *Science 139*, 223 (1963); C. H. Phoenix, *J. Comp. Physiol. Psychol. 54*, 72 (1961); R. W. Goy and C. H. Phoenix, *J. Reprod. Fertility 5*, 23 (1963); R. P. Michael, *Science 136*, 322 (1962).

43. C. D. Kochakian, *Lab. Invest. 8*, 538 (1959); A. Csapo, in *Cell, Organism, and Milieu*, D. Rudnick, Ed. (Ronald, New York, 1959), p. 107; P. Talalay and H. G. Williams-Ashman, *Proc. Natl. Acad. Sci. U.S. 44*, 15 (1958); C. A. Villee, in *Sex and Internal Secretions*, W. C. Young, Ed. (Williams and Wilkins, Baltimore, ed. 3, 1961), p. 643; J. T. Velardo, in *The Ovary*, H. G. Grady, Ed. (Williams and Wilkins, Baltimore, 1962), p. 48; R. J. Boscott, in *The Ovary*, S. S. Zukerman *et al.*, Eds. (Academic Press, New York, 1962), vol. 2, pp. 1, 47.

44. During the years in which the investigations discussed were in progress at Brown University, the Yale Laboratories of Primate Biology, and the University of Kansas, support was provided by the National Research Council's Committee for Research in Problems of Sex, and by grants, particularly MH-00504, from the National Institute of Mental Health, Bethesda, Md. Dr. Leon H. Schmidt, who at the time of this work was director of the Christ Hospital Institute for Medical Research, and Dr.

Harry F. Harlow, director of the Wisconsin Primate Research Center, extended the use of facilities in their laboratories for the production and study of female pseudohermaphroditic monkeys. Testosterone propionate (Perandren) was generously supplied by CIBA Pharmaceutical Corporation, Summit, N.J.

10

NEW FINDINGS RELEVANT TO THE EVOLUTION OF PSYCHOSEXUAL FUNCTIONS OF THE BRAIN *

Man finds himself in the predicament that Nature has endowed him essentially with three brains which, despite great differences in structure, must function together and communicate with one another. The oldest of these brains is basically reptilian. The second has been inherited from lower mammals, and the third is a late mammalian development, which in its culmination in primates, has made man peculiarly man.

Speaking allegorically of these three brains within a brain, we might imagine that when the psychiatrist bids the patient to lie on the couch, he is asking him to stretch out alongside a horse and a crocodile. The crocodile may be willing and ready to shed a tear and the horse to neigh and whinny, but when they are encouraged to express their troubles in words, it soon becomes evident that their inability is beyond the help of language training. Little wonder that the

---

* This article grew out of talks and lectures given to interdisciplinary psychiatric groups about work in progress on the cerebral representation of sexual functions.

patient who has personal responsibility for these animals and who must serve as their mouthpiece is sometimes accused of being full of resistances and reluctant to talk; or that the psychiatrist's interpretations and diagnosis suggest a certain lack of training in veterinary neuropsychiatry!

It may be expected that man will gain a better understanding of his animalistic brains when he learns more about their structure, chemistry and function. In this paper we shall be concerned with research that is attempting to solve some of the functional riddles of the lower mammalian brain. After a brief introduction to the problem, we shall describe some new findings on the representation of sexual functions in the lower mammalian brain. In the discussion we shall point out how these findings help in understanding certain neuropsychiatric observations regarding the primitive interplay of oral, aggressive and sexual behavior. This will lead to a description of some naturalistic observations on the sociosexual behavior of squirrel monkeys that will suggest, in conclusion, some implications of the experimental findings in regard to the evolution of psychosexual functions of the brain.

INTRODUCTORY BACKGROUND

In giving a little anatomical background for what is to follow, we can at the same time indicate some of the steps leading up to the recent findings. In support of the Papez theory (5, 10, 18), investigations of the last twenty years suggest that the lower mammalian brain which man shares with all mammals derives and acts upon information in terms of feelings, particularly emotional feelings that guide behavior with respect to the two basic life principles of *self-preservation* and *the preservation of the species* (9, 11).

The lower mammalian brain comprises the phylogenetically old cortex and its related nuclei. The designation of limbic system is applied to this lower mammalian brain because most of the old cortex is found in the great limbic lobe of Broca which surrounds the brain stem (6). Limbic means literally "forming a border around."

Figure 1, in which the brains of the rabbit, cat and monkey are drawn roughly to scale, illustrates that the limbic

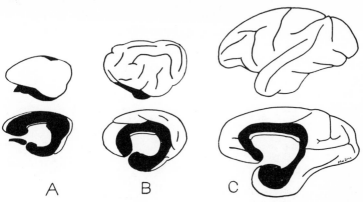

Figure 1. Most of the cortex of the "lower mammalian brain" is found in the limbic lobe. In this figure the brains of three commonly used experimental animals—rabbit (A), cat (B), and monkey (C)—illustrate that this lobe is found as a common denominator in the brains of all mammals. The cortex of the limbic lobe which surrounds the brain stem is represented in black. The neocortex which undergoes a dramatic mushrooming late in phylogeny is shown in white (from MacLean, P.D. In Wittkower, E. and Cleghorn, R., eds., *Recent Developments in Psychosomatic Medicine.* Pitman, London, 1954).

lobe is found as a common denominator in the brains of all mammals. The limbic cortex surrounding the brain stem is shown in black. The cortex of the new mammalian brain which mushrooms late in phylogeny is represented in white.

It should be emphasized that the limbic cortex is relatively crude and simple compared with the new cortex, and one might infer from this alone that it functions at an animalistic level in both animals and man. It should also be emphasized that in contrast to the new cortex, the limbic cortex has strong connections with the hypothalamus, which is so important in integrating the performance of mechanisms involved in self-preservation and procreation.

The rest of the anatomy that needs to be considered may be simplified if, as in Figure 2, the limbic system is pictured in a two-dimensional scheme. The stippled doughnut-shaped structure represents the limbic lobe itself. The drawing emphasizes that the medial forebrain bundle (MFB) is a

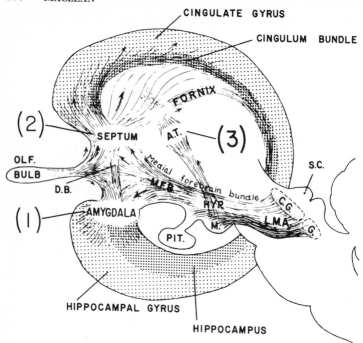

Figure 2. This diagram emphasizes that the medial forebrain bundle
(MFB) is a major line of communication between the limbic
lobe (in stipple) and the hypothalamus, midbrain and other
structures of the brain stem. Only ascending pathways of this
neural trunk are indicated. Major branchings to the amygdala,
septum and anterior thalamus are respectively designated by
the numerals 1, 2 and 3, and their significance is discussed
in the text. They supply the limbic cortex of the frontotemporal region, hippocampus and cingulate gyrus. The limbic
cortex, in turn, feeds back to the brain stem. Abbreviations:
A.T., anterior thalamic nuclei; C.G., central gray of midbrain;
D.B., diagonal band of Broca; G., ventral and dorsal teg-
mental nuclei of Gudden; HYP., hypothalamus; L.M.A., limbic
midbrain area of Nauta; M., mammillary body; PIT., pituitary; S.C., superior colliculus

major line of communication between the limbic lobe and the
brain stem. One might imagine that this bundle is like the
great trunk line of a railroad carrying traffic in opposite directions. Important stations are in the midbrain (LMA), hypothalamus (HYP), septum and amygdala.

Particular attention is drawn to three major branchings

of the medial forebrain bundle, indicated by the numerals. In giving emphasis to the above trunk-line analogy, the branch going "south" to the amygdala (No. 1) and its related cortex might be called the Great Southern Division of the limbic system. A corresponding emphasis should be given to the branch going in the opposite direction to the septum (No. 2) and its associated cortex. Finally, in view of the sexual findings to be described, attention is directed to a third large branch (No. 3), which arises in the hypothalamus and feeds into the anterior thalamus and the cingulate cortex. It will merit further comment in the discussion that this third branch has no counterpart in the reptilian brain, but appears for the first time in the mammal, and together with its associated nuclei and cortex reaches maximal development in man (2).

The classical ablation experiments of Klüver and Bucy showed that following bilateral ablations involving the amygdala division, wild monkeys become tame and docile and will eat food and nonfood objects indiscriminately (4). Such alterations in behavior would obviously be prejudicial to self-preservation in a natural environment. In stimulation studies, it has been demonstrated that stimulation at mixed points in this part of the brain elicits patterns of behavior that are related either to alimentary functions such as eating, swallowing and the like, or to searching, fighting and self-defense (6, 12). These findings indicate that mechanisms for eating and assimilating food are intimately geared in with those required for hunting and for angry attack, defense and escape called upon in the search for food.

In man the frontotemporal portion of the brain is vulnerable to birth injuries, head trauma and infections. In some individuals the subsequent scarring results in epileptogenic foci. The neuronal discharge triggered by these foci may elicit the same two general types of behavior seen when this part of the brain is stimulated in animals (6). In addition, from these tragic cases information about the subjective functions of this part of the brain can be derived. At the beginning of the discharge the individual may experience various feelings associated with threats to self-preservation. These may include terror, fear, sinking feelings, sensations of choking or a racing heart and sometimes anger. Or, in association with the alimentary automatisms, there may be a sense of odors, hunger, thirst or nausea. From the psychiatric point of view it should be emphasized that the interseizure symptomatology of some patients may be indistinguishable from that of schizophrenia. It should also be emphasized that there are indications that the neuronal discharge may be largely confined to the limbic system (7, 10).

From the foregoing observations it may be inferred that the frontotemporal division of the limbic system is largely concerned with self-preservation as it pertains to feeding and to the behavior involved in the struggle to obtain food (6).

One of the most striking features of the Klüver-Bucy syndrome is the bizarre hypersexuality that develops (4). It would appear that removal of the amygdala and related structures gives release, in the Jacksonian sense, to other parts of the brain concerned with sexual behavior.

In 1951, when we began to investigate the septal circuit of the limbic system (No. 2 in Figure 2) in cats, it was of signal interest to find that stimulation of the hippocampus and the anatomically related septum was frequently followed by enhanced pleasure and grooming reactions and sometimes penile erection (7–9). The general behavior was reminiscent of that of courtship in male cats. These findings, together with complementary observations in the rat, suggested that this part of the limbic system was concerned with expressive and feeling states that are conducive to sociability and other preliminaries of copulation and reproduction. In other words, close to the amygdala was a system of structures that seemed to be involved *in sustaining the species rather than the self.*

RECENT FINDINGS

In view of the complexities of sociosexual behavior involved in the preservation of the species, it is a curious fact that there has existed little evidence of representation of sexual functions above the primitive level of the hypothalamus. A concern for the welfare and preservation of the species is based on sexuality, and in man it reflects itself in a multiplicity of ways. It is a concern that leads to courtship and the eventual rearing of the family. It is a concern that permeates our songs, our poetry, our novels, art, theatre, architecture. It is a concern that preoccupies us in planning for the higher education of our children. It is a concern that promotes the building of libraries, institutes of research, and hospitals. It is a concern that inspires medical research to prevent suffering and dying of patients who have not yet become sick or old. It is a concern that makes us think in terms of rockets, travel in outer space, and the possibility of immortal life in some other world.

We shall now present some recent findings that support the obvious assumption that Nature did not stop at the primitive level of the hypothalamus, but has endowed man, and mammals generally, with considerable brain stem and cortex with which to promote the preservation of the species. In a continuation of brain stimulation studies on the cerebral representation of sexual functions, the writer has been mapping structures involved in such sexual functions as penile erection, seminal discharge and genital scratching. First we shall describe experiments in which penile erection has been used as one indicator that a structure is implicated in sexual behavior (14).

For pursuing this work, it was desirable to use an animal more akin to man than the carnivore. We chose the squirrel monkey (Saimiri sciureus) because this little New World primate, which weighs as little as the guinea pig, has a brain comparable to the cat's in size and therefore of desirable dimensions for neuroanatomical and neurophysiological studies.

A special platform is fixed to the animal's head which allows one to explore the brain millimeter by millimeter while the animal sits peacefully in a restraining chair. During an experimental day two electrodes are lowered millimeter by millimeter, and stimulation is applied alternately at each point with a variety of stimulus parameters. Electrodes are returned to positive points and fixed in place so that stimulation and recording can be repeated on subsequent days. Because of previous findings in the cat, the bioelectrical activity of the hippocampus is monitored routinely.

Figure 3 shows on brain diagrams the positive loci for erection found in the first study (14). The positive points are represented by diamonds and squares. The squares give the added information that penile erection was associated with hippocampal afterdischarges. The open, half-filled and solid symbols denote gradations from partial to full erection. The vertical dashes represent points explored and found to be negative. It is to be emphasized that all points are checked histologically in stained serial sections of the brain.

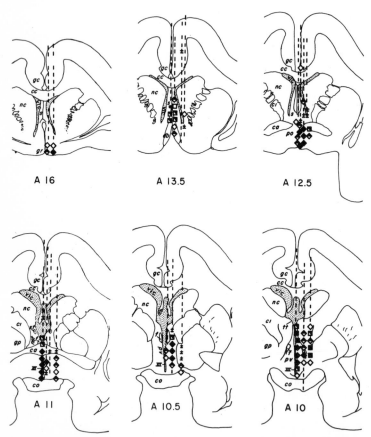

Figure 3.   Diamonds and squares in above diagrams of cross-sections through squirrel monkey brain show loci at which electrical stimulation elicited penile erection. Squares give the added information that stimulation was followed by electrical after-discharges in hippocampus. The open, half-filled and solid symbols denote gradations from partial to full erection. Verti-

In subsequent studies the brain rostral and caudal to the levels shown in Figure 3 was explored. In summary, the positive loci for erection in the forebrain and diencephalon are found distributed along parts of three corticosubcortical subdivisions of the limbic system enumerated in Figure 4. First, there is evidence that they coincide with the distribution

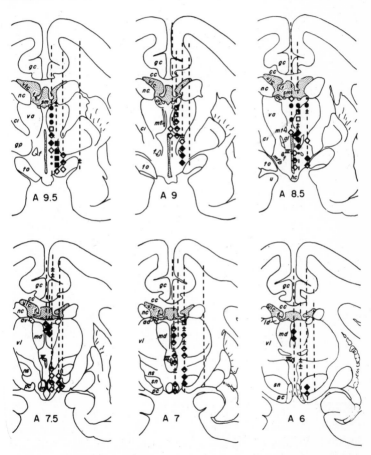

cal dashes indicate points explored and found to be negative. In a more recent study strongly positive points have been found in the cingulate gyrus just rostral to the knee of the corpus callosum. For further details see original paper (from MacLean, P. D. and Ploog, D. W. Cerebral representation of penile erection. *J. Neurophysiol.*, 25: 29–55, 1962).

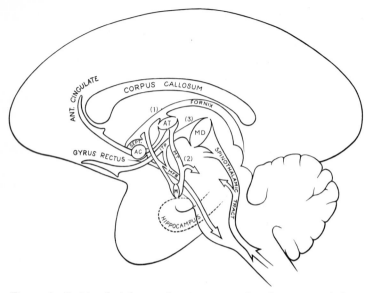

Figure 4. Positive loci for penile erection are found in parts of three
corticosubcortical subdivisions of the limbic system that are
schematically depicted in above drawing and labeled 1, 2 and
3. See text for definition. The septum (SEPT) and medial
part of medial dorsal nucleus (MD) are nodal points with
respect to erection. The medial forebrain bundle (MFB) and
inferior thalamic peduncle (ITP) are important descending
pathways. The drawing also schematizes recently demonstrated connections (5) of the spinothalamic pathway with
the medial dorsal nucleus and intralaminar nuclei. Scratching
of the genitals and/or ejaculation have been elicited by stimulation at various points along this pathway and regions of its
termination in the foregoing structures. Other abbreviations:
AC, anterior commissure; AT, anterior thalamus; M, mammillary bodies.

of known hippocampal projections to parts of the septum,
anterior thalamus and hypothalamus. Second, they have been
located in parts of the so-called Papez circuit (18), comprising the mammillary bodies, the mammillothalamic tract, the
anterior thalamic nuclei and anterior cingulate gyrus. Finally,
they have been found in parts of the medial orbital gyrus, the
medial part of the medial dorsal nucleus of the thalamus and
regions of their known connections.

In regard to this last finding it is pertinent to recall that frontal lobotomy, which severs the connections between the medial dorsal nucleus and the orbitofrontal and prefrontal cortex, sometimes results in bizarre, uninhibited sexual behavior.

The medial part of the medial dorsal nucleus and the medial septopreoptic region appear to be nodal points for erection. The experimental findings indicate that the medial forebrain bundle is the major descending pathway from these nodal points (*cf.* Figure 4). We need not be concerned here with the further downward course which we have traced from the diencephalon into the midbrain and pons (13).

Stimulations in the septum and rostral diencephalon which result in erection (Figure 3) are commonly associated with afterdischarges in the hippocampus (14). During these afterdischarges, erections may become throbbing in character and reach maximum size. For several minutes following afterdischarges one may see abnormal spiking activity in the hippocampus, and during this time there may be waxing and waning of partial penile erection for periods commonly as long as five minutes, and sometimes as long as ten minutes. Such findings suggest that the hippocampus modifies the excitability of effector neurons involved in penile erection.

Comparable to our previous observations in the cat (8, 9) it has been striking to observe how apparently calm, contented and placid an aggressive monkey becomes after a number of these hippocampal afterdischarges have been elicited. The apparent changes in mood may last for several hours. Some of the implications of these studies in regard to the self-stimulation experiments of Olds and Milner (17) and others have been discussed elsewhere (11).

Despite the somewhat orgastic appearance of the erection associated with hippocampal afterdischarges, ejaculation is not seen under these circumstances. This recalls the evidence that erection is a parasympathetic phenomenon whereas ejaculation depends on sympathetic mechanisms. In mapping the brain stem we have encountered a number of points in the thalamus and along the course of the spinothalamic pathway at which stimulation elicits seminal discharge with motile sperm (13) and quasi-pruritic scratching of the genitalia. The positive points in the thalamus are in structures lying within and bordering upon the caudal intralaminar region. These include the central lateral nucleus and the contiguous parts of the medial dorsal nucleus and parafascicular-centre median complex. These are the same structures to which neuroanatomists have recently traced the medial division of the spinothalamic tract (1, 15).

Seminal discharge may occur independently of genital scratching and anticipate the appearance of throbbing penile erection. In the thalamus positive points for this response were localized in the ventromedial part of the medial dorsal nucleus and the mid-dorsal portion of the parafascicular-centre median complex. Within a millimeter of a positive point for seminal discharge, stimulation might elicit other visceromotor effects such as salivation, vomiting, urination and defecation.

As summarized schematically in Figure 4, the findings suggest that thalamic structures involved in genital sensation and ejaculation lie in proximity to and probably articulate with the part of the medial dorsal nucleus that is nodal with respect to penile erection. One might think of the former structures as primitive somatosensory nuclei linked to visceromotor and endocrine motor nuclei in the hypothalamus by the inferior thalamic peduncle and the periventricular fiber system. It is to be noted that the intralaminar structures involved are part of the so-called "diffuse (or non-specific) projection system."

DISCUSSION

Oral-genital relationships: Figure 2 schematizes the proximity of the amygdala and septum, which, as the stimulation experiments have shown, are involved in oral and sexual functions, respectively. The amygdala has strong connections with the septum and, as Nauta has shown (16), with the medial dorsal nucleus as well. In the continuation of our investigations it has been of interest to find that by stimulating parts of the amygdala one may obtain chewing and salivation, with partial erection occurring as a recruited response after many seconds of stimulation or as a rebound phenomenon after stimulation is terminated (20). In other words, excitation in a region involved in oral mechanisms readily spills over into others concerned with genital function.

This close neural relationship helps in understanding the intimate interplay of behavior in the oral and sexual spheres, examples of which we are accustomed to see in the activities of our domestic animals. Such an interplay is readily taken for granted in animals, but one has only to consider the last fifty years of Freudian psychiatry to realize the trouble that it may lead to in human affairs.

If there is any neural offender that can be blamed for this situation, then the olfactory sense, more than any other, must be considered the culprit (11). When the animal is viewed in the ordinary elongated position, the oral and anogenital regions appear to be at opposite poles. A corresponding relation is maintained in the topographical representation of the body in the post-central gyrus of the neocortex. In the organization of the lower mammalian brain, however, Nature apparently found it necessary to bend the limbic lobe upon itself in order to afford the olfactory sense close participation in both oral and anogenital functions.

Sexuality, fear and aggression: The foregoing considerations are germane to the close connection between sexuality and fear and aggression. As is well recognized, fighting is frequently a preliminary to both feeding and mating. One sees combative behavior even in the nursing babe which will angrily fight the breast if no milk is forthcoming, and at the same time develop penile erection. Proceeding caudally from the level of the anterior commissure, one can follow neural structures involved in fearful or angry, combative behavior lying proximal to those concerned with feeding and sexual responses. Within the space of a millimeter, one may pass from a point at which stimulation results in erection and an apparent state of placidity to one at which the electrical current elicits erection in conjunction with an angry or fearful type of vocalization and showing of fangs (14). As one lowers the electrode a little deeper, one may obtain only fearful or angry-appearing manifestations during stimulation, yet see erection appear as a rebound phenomenon after stimulation is terminated.

One is reminded of a statement in Freud's *Three Contributions to the Theory of Sex:* "The sexually exciting influence of some painful affects such as fear, shuddering, and horror is felt by a great many people throughout life and readily explains why so many seek opportunities to experience such sensations. . . ." (3, p. 62). One thinks of pyromania, for example.

A few additional quotations from this same monograph will serve to introduce some naturalistic observations on the squirrel monkey that are relevant to the close relationship of sexual and aggressive behavior. In discussing the origins of the sexual impulse, Freud mentions the looking impulse and the cruelty impulse.

In regard to the looking impulse, he says, "The little child is above all shameless, and during its early years it evinces definite pleasure in displaying its body and especially its sexual organs. A counterpart to this desire . . . is . . . the curiosity to see other persons' genitals. . . . I must conclude that the impulse for looking can appear in the child as a spontaneous sexual manifestation" (3).

Freud discusses the cruelty component of the sexual impulse and makes the observation that "children who are distinguished for evincing especial cruelty to animals and playmates may be justly suspected of intensive and premature sexual activity in the erogenous zones." A few pages later he remarks: "A number of persons report that they experienced the first signs of excitement in their genitals during fighting or wrestling with playmates. . . . The infantile connection between fighting and sexual excitement acts in many persons as a determinant for the future preferred course of their sexual impulse" (3).

Some relevant naturalistic observations: These comments on the looking and cruelty impulse have comparative interest relevant to a study of the social behavior of the squirrel monkey that we have conducted in parallel with our stimulation experiments. Figure 5 shows a group of six monkeys

Figure 5. Group of six squirrel monkeys (four males and two females) that was used in the behavioral study described in text. Throughout the year of observation they lived in the Plexiglas viewing cage shown here. The dominant male, Caspar, is on the floor at the right next to the food dish; Edgar, lowest in rank of the males, is in left-hand corner (from Ploog, D. W. and MacLean, P. D. Penile display in the squirrel monkey [Saimiri sciureus]. *Anim. Behav., 11:* 32–39, 1963).

which, with Dr. Detlev Ploog and others, we observed for over a year in an attempt to evaluate and quantify certain aspects of their behavior. As shown, the four males and two females lived in a Plexiglas house with a plastic tree in the middle.

Among the most interesting things brought to light by this study was the finding that the squirrel monkey displays penile erection under a variety of conditions (19). It is commonly performed at a distance by two strange animals, presumably as a kind of greeting. The same pattern of display may occur when a mirror is held up before a monkey. In the communal situation the male may display penile erection in juxtaposition to a female or to another male. In each case, as illustrated in Figure 6, the display is performed with the thighs spread and the erect penis thrust almost into the face of the other animal. In the case of two males, if the recipient does not remain quiet and submissive during the display, it may be viciously assaulted by the displaying animal. On the basis of special studies it was concluded that such display is used as a means of exerting and establishing dominance. Indeed, it was found to be a better measure of dominance than the outcome of rivalry for food. The display to a female appears to be part of courtship, as it is seen preceding attempts at copulation.

Caspar, the animal which proved to be the dominant male in the colony, displayed to all the other males but none in turn displayed to him. In contrast, Edgar, the male lowest in rank, displayed to none of the other males, but all displayed to him. Edgar displayed only to humans!

The bodily orientation of two monkeys during the display is somewhat reminiscent of two dogs mutually smelling the genitalia. But the emphasis in the monkey appears to be on visual, rather than olfactory cues. It is to be remembered that the dog is dominated to a large extent by its olfactory sense, whereas the monkey is dominated by its visual sense. It would almost seem that the squirrel monkey is a primate form representing, as it were, a "missing link" between the macrosmatic animal and the visually dominant animal.

The finding that the squirrel monkey assumes the same

Figure 6.   In the communal situation, the male squirrel monkey may display penile erection in the act of courtship, or, as illustrated
above, it may display to another male as a means of exerting
and establishing dominance. In each case the display is performed with the thighs spread and the erect penis thrust
almost into the face of the other animal (from Ploog, D. W.
and MacLean, P. D. Penile display in the squirrel monkey
[Saimiri sciureus] *Anim. Behav., 11:* 32–39, 1963).

posture of penile display in courtship and aggression has special phylogenetic interest when it is recalled that the sexual
posturing of some male fishes and birds is indistinguishable
from their aggressive posturing. The observations of Freud
remind us that remnants of the looking and seeing impulses
and the impulse to mastery are found in man. In Biblical times
such a connection with mastery is illustrated in Genesis, 24:2,
in which Abraham says to his eldest servant, "Put I pray thee,
thy hand under my thigh: And I will make thee swear . . .
that thou shall not take a wife unto my son of the daughters

of the Canaanites." Thigh, it is said, is used here euphemistically for the genitals.[1]

Might one infer from these various observations on monkey and man that genital display and the impulse to mastery are built into the neural apparatus of the primate? If so, it would have relevance to the age-old question of why man developed a sense of modesty and chose to cover himself. Is it not possible that man with his superior intelligence discovered that by assuming the fig leaf, and later the loin cloth, he was able to reduce the unpleasant social tension created by the show of these aggressive impulses? Perhaps this has facilitated acculturation on the long hard road to civilization.

There are other considerations that lead one to wonder if penile display does not generalize to the eye, so that the mere act of one animal looking into the eyes of another becomes in itself an aggressive act. Some monkeys, such as the macaque, seem in general to try to avoid looking each other in the eye, or indeed looking people in the eye. If you look the macaque in the eye, it will charge you. In this connection it is interesting to recall that looking in the eye spells panic to some patients and particularly some schizophrenic patients. They find it impossible to follow the half-polite, half-aggressive social dictum inculcated from an early age, of looking people straight in the eye.

Sexuality and altruism: Thus far we have considered neural and behavioral findings that would appear to shed some light on psychiatric observations that the acts of mastering, devouring and procreating seem to be inextricably tied to one another.

In concluding, we have yet to consider a subject that goes to the roots of man's idealism and altruism—namely, the close connection of feeding, sustaining and sexuality. A concern for the welfare and preservation of the species is based on sexuality. The mother when feeding her baby at breast experiences well-being and may have sensations associated with tumescence in the genital region. Subjective analyses have

---

[1] I am grateful to Dr. Samuel Nelken for calling my attention to this passage and pointing out its significance.

shown that there may be a comparable reaction in the feelings of those who find joy in helping and sustaining others.

In giving the results of the stimulation studies we pointed out that penile erection was obtained by stimulating structures along the course of the mammillothalamic tract and in parts of the anterior and medial thalamic nuclei (14). Heretofore these structures have been looked upon as silent areas of the brain. The mammillothalamic pathway, the pathway numbered three in Figure 2, is, as LeGros Clark and Meyer emphasized, not found in the reptilian brain but appears for the first time in the mammal (2). It is possibly pertinent to the increasingly complicated sociosexual behavior that one finds in ascending the phylogenetic scale of the mammal, that this pathway and its related nuclei attain their greatest size in man. Thus there seems to be support for the assumption that Nature did not stop at the primitive level of the hypothalamus, but endowed us with considerable brain stem and cortex with which to promote the preservation of the species.

It may be particularly significant that the medial dorsal nucleus which projects to the orbital and prefrontal cortex develops in association with the anterior group of nuclei and literally embraces them. As pointed out, the ancient midline portion of the medial dorsal nucleus is implicated in penile erection. Indeed, it is such a potent point that stimulation here may elicit close to full erection even under deep anesthesia (14).

The prefrontal cortex, which is connected to the medial dorsal nucleus, is a relatively recent addition to the new mammalian brain. From our limited knowledge of its functions, it might be inferred that it is largely concerned with anticipation and planning as it pertains to both self-preservation and preservation of the species. From the latter standpoint, it should be noted that it requires not only much foresight, but also a long deferment of gratification (in neural terms, a great deal of inhibition) to keep planning and working as Jacob did for 14 years for Rachel and the anticipated progeny of that union. It requires a far higher order of extrapolation and a far deeper concern for the species to work as those in the medical sciences are working, not only for patients currently under treatment, but also through research for the progeny that we wish to prevent from suffering and dying in years to come.

In the complex organization of the old and new structures under consideration, we presumably have a neural ladder, a visionary ladder, for ascending from the most primitive sexual feeling to the highest level of altruistic sentiments.

SUMMARY

This paper summarizes recent findings of brain stimulation studies on the cerebral representation of sexual functions. In the squirrel monkey penile erection is elicited by stimulation within parts of three cortico-subcortical subdivisions of the limbic system. Seminal discharge with motile sperm and/or quasi-pruritic genital scratching results from stimulation at points within and bordering upon the caudal intralaminar region of the thalamus, as well as along the course of the spinothalamic pathway. The findings suggest that thalamic structures involved in ejaculation and genital sensation lie in close proximity to, and probably articulate with, those that are nodal with respect to penile erection.

In the discussion it is pointed out that these observations, combined with what is known about oral representation, attest to the close organization of oral and sexual functions in the brain. There is also evidence that structures involved in oral and sexual functions lie in juxtaposition to those concerned with fearful and combative behavior. These findings would seem to help in understanding the primitive interplay of oral, aggressive and sexual behavior.

In commenting upon the relationship of sexuality and aggression, some naturalistic observations on display of penile erection in the squirrel monkey are described. Reminiscent of the behavior of some fishes and birds, the posture of the display is the same in courtship as in the preliminary show of aggression towards other males. The role of vision in the display recalls Freud's comments on the looking and cruelty components of the sexual impulse in children. This leads in conclusion to a consideration of the neural and behavioral findings from the standpoint of the evolution of psychosexual functions of the brain. Some speculations are made in regard to man's assumption of the loin cloth.

REFERENCES

1. Anderson, F. D. and Berry, C. M. Degeneration studies of long ascending fiber systems in the cat brain stem. *J. Comp. Neurol., 111:* 195–230, 1959.
2. Clark, W. E. LeGros and Meyer, M. Anatomical relationships between the cerebral cortex and the hypothalamus. *Brit. Med. Bull., 6:* 341–344, 1950.
3. Freud, S. *Three contributions to the theory of sex.* Tr. by A. A. Brill. Nervous and Mental Disease Monogr., New York, 1948.
4. Klüver, H. and Bucy, P. C. Preliminary analysis of functions of the temporal lobe in monkeys. *Arch. Neurol. Psychiat., 42:* 979–1000, 1939.
5. MacLean, P. D. Psychosomatic disease and the "visceral brain": Recent developments bearing on the Papez theory of emotion. *Psychosom. Med., 11:* 338–353, 1949.
6. MacLean, P. D. Some psychiatric implications of physiological studies on frontotemporal portion of limbic system (visceral brain). *Electroenceph. Clin. Neurophysiol., 4:* 407–418, 1952.
7. MacLean, P. D. The limbic system ("visceral brain") in relation to central gray and reticulum of the brain stem: Evidence of interdependence in emotional processes. *Psychosom. Med., 17:* 355–366, 1955.
8. MacLean, P. D. Chemical and electrical stimulation of hippocampus in unrestrained animals. Part II: Behavioral findings. *A. M. A. Arch. Neurol. Psychiat., 78:* 128–142, 1957.
9. MacLean, P. D. The limbic system with respect to self-preservation and the preservation of the species. *J. Nerv. Ment. Dis., 127:* 1–11, 1958.
10. MacLean, P. D. Contrasting functions of limbic and neocortical systems of the brain and their relevance to psychophysiological aspects of medicine. *Amer. J. Med., 25:* 611–626, 1958.
11. MacLean, P. D. The limbic system with respect to two basic life principles. In Brazier, M. A. B., ed. *The Central Nervous System and Behavior,* pp. 31–118. Josiah Macy Jr. Foundation, New York, 1959.
12. MacLean, P. D. and Delgado, J. M. R. Electrical and chemical stimulation of frontotemporal portion of limbic system in the waking animal. *Electroenceph. Clin. Neurophysiol., 5:* 91–100, 1953.
13. MacLean, P. D., Dua, S. and Denniston, R. H. Dienmesencephalic loci involved in penile erection and seminal discharge (abstract). *Fed. Proc., 20:* 331–C, 1961.

14. MacLean, P. D. and Ploog, D. W. Cerebral representation of penile erection. *J. Neurophysiol., 25:* 29–55, 1962.

15. Mehler, W. H., Feferman, M. E. and Nauta, W. J. H. Ascending axon degeneration following anterolateral cordotomy: An experimental study in the monkey. *Brain, 83:* 718–750, 1960.

16. Nauta, W. J. H. Anatomical relationships between the amygdaloid complex, the dorsomedial thalamic nucleus and the orbitofrontal cortex in monkey (abstract). *Anat. Rec., 136:* 251, 1960.

17. Olds, J. and Milner, P. Positive reinforcement produced by electrical stimulation of septal area and other regions of the rat brain. *J. Comp. Physiol. Psychol., 47:* 419–427, 1954.

18. Papez, J. W. A proposed mechanism of emotion. *A. M. A. Arch. Neurol. Psychiat., 38:* 725–743, 1937.

19. Ploog, D. W. and MacLean, P. D. Penile display in the squirrel monkey (Saimiri sciureus). *Anim. Behav., 11:* 32–39, 1963.

20. Reis, D. J., Carmichael, M. and MacLean, P. D. Cerebral representation of genital function. IV: Frontotemporal region. (Unpublished.)

11

CEREBRAL IMPLANTATION AND
AUTORADIOGRAPHIC STUDIES
OF SEX HORMONES *

The importance of the hypothalamus for the control of reproduction in mammals has been made clear by an abundance of research employing the techniques of brain lesions, electrical stimulation, and electrical recording. Two reviews by Harris (1955, 1962) cite the evidence that neural tissue and portal vessels of the median eminence and pituitary stalk transmit the influences of the central nervous system and circulating hormones to the anterior pituitary gland, thus regulating production or release of tropic hormones. Sawyer (1960) has reviewed the lesion experiments which lead to the conclusion that the hypothalamus mediates the effect of sex hormones on mating behavior as well as controlling the gonadotropic activity of the pituitary. From results with male rats, cats, and guinea pigs he suggested that two separate hypo-

* This paper was written during the term of a Public Health Service predoctoral fellowship, #1-F1-MH-21, 337–01, awarded by the National Institute of Mental Health. Supplementary aid was received from NASA grant #Nsg 496.

thalamic centers serve these two functions: the removal of one center abolishes mating behavior, and destruction of the other slows the production of gonadotropins.

In the last eight years sex hormones, the natural stimuli of reproductive mechanisms, have been applied to the brain in order to investigate further how those mechanisms are controlled. On the one hand, implantation of minute amounts of sex hormone into the brain permits precise localization of effective sites, without the complications which obscure interpretation of ablation experiments. In lesion experiments, for instance, the irritation of tissue around the lesion, rather than the actual removal of tissue, may cause the postoperative changes observed (Reynolds, 1963). On the other hand, autoradiography yields information about uptake within individual cells after injection of labeled hormones, and still allows study of the entire brain in a single experiment.

IMPLANTATION OF SEX HORMONES INTO THE BRAIN

Investigators using the technique of hormone implantation in the brain have usually directed their attention either to the role of the hypothalamus in controlling anterior pituitary function or to the direct hypothalamic control of mating behavior.

Effect of Hormone Implants on Pituitary Gonadotropic Activity: Recently, Flerko (1957, 1963; Flerko and Szentagothai, 1957) has extended the evidence for the feedback of gonadal steroids to the brain, where they inhibit gonadotropic function. The earliest suggestions of this negative feedback arose from pioneer work thirty years ago (Meyer, Leonard, Hisaw, and Martin, 1932; Moore and Price, 1932) and postulated feedback directly to the pituitary, but more recent data point to the hypothalamus as an additional receptor site for circulating sex hormones. Flerko and Szentagothai (1957) autografted small ovarian fragments into the anterior hypothalamus in female rats with the result of significantly decreased uterine weight, indicating a decline in gonadotropin secretion. Effective sites of implantation were always close to the ventricle in the anterior hypothalamus, which is consistent with Flerko's (1957) finding that this specific paraventricular region must be intact if estrogen injections in female rats are to reduce the postcastration burst of gonadotropin secretion. A host of ablation studies (see Flerko, 1963), showing that female rats with paraventricular lesions in the anterior hypothalamus remain in constant estrus, supports the notion that ovarian hormones exert their negative feedback in that region. Since these lesioned animals usually had cystic follicles but no corpora lutea, the loss of midline anterior hypothalamic tissue probably allows uninhibited production of FSH.

Lisk (1960) placed small crystals of estradiol in various hypothalamic nuclei of adult rats to find which sites would mediate the hormone's effect on the weights of organs in the genital tracts of males and females. Only implants in the arcuate nucleus of the hypothalamus, in males and females, and in the mammillary bodies, in females, caused decreases in the weights of their respective sexual organs. Thus, the arcuate nucleus and the mammillary bodies were the only sites where gonadotropin output was inhibited. These results are not inconsistent with Flerko's findings because Lisk's anterior hypothalamic implants were not as close to the ventricle as Flerko's were. Testosterone implants into the hypothalamus gave essentially the same results, the arcuate nucleus being the only effective site in both sexes (Lisk, 1962a). In females the mammillary bodies were not thoroughly enough probed with testosterone implants to conclude that they cannot mediate the effect of testosterone on the anterior pituitary. In both the estradiol and the testosterone experiments, decrease of sexual organ weights was accompanied by histological signs of atrophy in those organs.

Lisk's main finding with testosterone in male rats has been replicated with male dogs by Davidson and Sawyer (1961). Their implants, too, in the posterior median eminence resulted in significantly decreased testicular weight and a histological appearance of atrophy, and other placements were ineffective. Notably, pituitary sites of implantation did not cause testicular or prostatic changes.

Lisk has continued to investigate some aspects of the inhibitory effect of estrogen as mediated by the arcuate nucleus. Estradiol implants in the arcuate inhibit or reverse the formation of castration cells in the anterior pituitary of previously ovariectomized female rats (Lisk, 1962b), and only in this site can the hormone preserve normal pituitary weight and histological appearance (Lisk, 1963a). In his analysis of how estradiol affects the function of the anterior pituitary through the arcuate nucleus, Lisk (1963b) has made use of Leveque's (1953) and Edström's (1957) finding that nucleolar size varies directly with the activity of the neuron. Lisk found that estradiol implantation in the arcuate nucleus significantly reduced the average diameters of nucleoli in that region and therefore inhibited gonadotropin output by decreasing neural activity in this hypothalamic nucleus. This result is in striking agreement with Ifft's (1962) finding that only the arcuate nucleus showed consistent decrease in nucleolar size in female rats maintained by experimental manipulations in prolonged diestrus, when compared to nucleolar size in a group of constant estrus rats. Ablation of the arcuate nucleus has the same effect as implanting estradiol in it: atrophy of the gonads (Dey, 1943). Thus, estradiol probably cuts down the excitation of the anterior pituitary by the arcuate, as Lisk inferred.

The regions of sensitivity to estradiol found by Flerko and Szentagothai (1957) in the anterior hypothalamus near the ventricle and by Lisk (1960) in the arcuate nucleus may represent two points in a single hypothalamic region concerned with gonadotropin release, for effective pituitary control has been demonstrated at an intermediate site. Knigge (1962) implanted pituitary glands of neonatal rats in various hypothalamic areas of hypophysectomized adult male rats and studied the viable grafts and hormone functions in the hosts three months later. Although no evidence was found for the secretion of thyroid or adrenal tropic hormones by the grafts, pituitaries placed in the floor of the hypothalamus interrupting or encroaching upon fibers of the supraopticohypophyseal tract supported active spermatogenesis and caused a significant increase in testicular weight compared to the hypophysectomized group without grafts. All other sites of pituitary grafts were ineffective. One interpretation of this experiment is that the grafts releasing gonadotropin were situated in the middle of a region extending from the medial anterior hypothalamus (Flerko and Szentagothai, 1957) to the arcuate nucleus or mammillary bodies (Lisk, 1960), and that neurons throughout this region receive circulating gonadal hormones and produce releasing factors for gonadotropins. However, the grafts may have merely ruptured axons carrying releasing factors from the medial anterior hypothalamus to the median eminence.

In the past year studies have been reported which combine the method of hormone implantation with assays for specific gonadotropins in an effort to delimit further the mechanism of hormonal feedback. In female rabbits Kanematsu and Sawyer (1963a) found that estradiol benzoate implanted in the posterior median eminence caused a marked decrease in pituitary LH (luteinizing hormone) content, as measured by the depletion of ovarian ascorbic acid. Pituitary implants of estrogen had no effect on LH content. Since Ramirez, Abrams, and McCann (1963) found that tuberal estradiol implants prevented the usual postcastration rise in plasma and urinary LH in ovariectomized rats, Kanematsu and Sawyer's result is probably due to a decreased synthesis of LH rather than a sudden release of LH into the plasma from the pituitary. Median eminence lesions in female rats as well as median eminence estradiol implants in female rabbits cause depletion of pituitary LH (Taleisnik and McCann, 1961), suggesting that this specific effect on LH is mediated by disappearance of an excitatory substance traveling from or through the median eminence to the anterior pituitary.

Kanematsu and Sawyer (1963b) have made a similar study on the effect of tuberal estradiol implants on prolactin synthesis and release in rabbits. Such implants caused a large increase in pituitary prolactin content, measured by the increase in crop sac weight of squabs after injections of rabbit pituitary homogenate. However, the mammary glands of the implanted rabbits were not activated, so the estradiol either increased the synthesis without increasing release of prolactin or it simply blocked release and allowed prolactin to accumulate in the pituitary. Estradiol implanted directly into the pituitary did cause prolactin release, as measured by mammary gland activation. It would seem that only the effect of progesterone implants need be discovered, to add to the foregoing results with estradiol and the knowledge that pituitary grafts continue to secrete prolactin independent of the hypothalamus (Everett, 1956), in order to determine a comprehensive model of prolactin control.

To sum up the findings on sex-hormone implantation in the brain: Flerko and Szentagothai (1957) and Lisk (1960, 1962a) have identified areas where gonadal steroids inhibit gonadotropin output in the midline anterior hypothalamus and the arcuate nucleus, respectively, and at least one site concerned with gonadotropin release may lie between them (Knigge, 1962). Kanematsu and Sawyer (1963a, 1963b) have made use of the effective implantation site in the median eminence to study the control of LH and prolactin by estradiol.

Effects of Hormone Implants on Mating Behavior: Some investigators have used sex hormones to identify the neural pathways that direct sexual behavior. In 1956 Fisher reported that by injecting small amounts of testosterone sulfate into the lateral preoptic area of male or female rats he could induce exaggerated male mating responses. Within minutes of the time of injection the injected rat would try to mount a partner. The mating behavior following these injections was unusual in its speed and compulsiveness. If injections were made into the medial, instead of the lateral, preoptic area, males as well as females would show more or less coordinated elements of maternal behavior, usually nest building with paper strips and retrieving. Some rats with injections in intermediate sites attempted to carry on maternal and mating behavior at the same time or behaved in a diffusely excited manner. With this technique animals could be made to behave *in vacuo*—they might try to "retrieve" their tail or their adult partner—but in the presence of adequate stimuli the entire hierarchy of maternal or mating behavior could be elicited. Vaughan and Fisher (1962) have extended these studies, reporting that electrical stimulation in the anterior dorsolateral hypothalamus produces a marked increase in male sexual behavior in male rats.

At the same time as Fisher's original study, Harris, Michael, and Scott (1958) were performing similar experiments using hypothalamic implants of diethylstilbestrol in ovariectomized female cats. The dibutyrate ester of diethylstilbestrol was used to demonstrate that such cats would accept males and show lordosis after implantation in the posterior hypothalamus but not after subcutaneous placement of an equal amount of the chemical. The failure of the subcutaneous placement and the anestrous condition of the genital tract during mating suggested that the estrogen worked through a local neural mechanism in the posterior hypothalamus and not through the systemic circulation. Other sites of implantation in the brain were ineffective. The rate of diffusion from the implant was critical, for its increase by the use of the dipropionate ester or by increase of surface area of the implant caused both subcutaneous and hypothalamic implants to be effective. Likewise, a slower diffusion rate, as from the dilaurate ester of diethylstilbestrol, prevented implants, even in the posterior hypothalamus, from inducing mating responses. Lisk (1962a) also noted that testosterone implants in the arcuate nucleus of male rats caused a much greater degree of atrophy in the genital tract when implants of larger surface area, affording a higher rate of diffusion, were used.

By measuring ultraviolet light absorption of the hormone left on the implant needle after mating, Michael (1961) estimated the amount left and from this result determined that effective sites in the hypothalamus were not distinguished from ineffective locations in the nervous system by their rates of hormone diffusion. That is, while Harris, Michael, and Scott (1958) and Lisk (1962a) found that a given region could begin to respond to the hormone if its rate of diffusion was increased, for a given hormone and with other conditions held constant effective sites evoke the same rate of diffusion as ineffective sites. Similarly, the distance of spread of C^{14}-diethylstilbestrol dibutyrate, measured on auto-radiograms, was the same in effective and ineffective locations. Thus, a mechanism for the expression of mating behavior appears to exist in the hypothalamus, activated hormonally, independent of the two biophysical parameters for which Michael has controlled.

One complication introduced by these results of Harris, Michael, and Scott comes from the failure of preoptic implantations of diethylstilbestrol to induce mating. On the basis of Sawyer and Robison's (1956) ablation experiment in female cats, the anterior hypothalamus would have been expected to initiate mating responses as a consequence of hormone stimulation, for lesions there resulted in permanent behavioral anestrus despite treatment with exogenous estrogen. This discrepancy would be sharper if some of Sawyer and Robison's lesions had been placed farther anterior, in the preoptic area, where Harris, Michael, and Scott's negative results were obtained.

Better agreement of results from implant and lesion methods is found in experiments on female rats. The only sites in the hypothalamus at which estradiol implantations elicit lordosis reflexes in ovariectomized female rats are in the anterior hypothalamus and the preoptic area near the midline (Lisk, 1962c), the same region in which lesions disrupt mating behavior in the females of this species (Clark, 1942).

The technique of hormone implantations in the brain is now being extended to study a wider variety of behavioral phenomena that depend upon the levels of circulating hormones. Mr. Barry Komisaruk, of Rutgers University (Komisaruk, 1964), is implanting progesterone in the brains of ring doves in an attempt to elicit parental incubation of eggs, which is known to follow systemic injections of progesterone (Lehrman and Wortis, 1960). Of forty-six birds thus far implanted, nine showed incubation behavior, two of which had received implants in the anterior hypothalamus and five of which were implanted in tracts connecting the anterior hypothalamus to the archistriatum (homologous to the mammalian amygdala). Nine of the twenty-three males implanted stopped courtship behavior in the manner that follows systemic progesterone injection (Komisaruk, 1964), but there was no pattern detected in the localization of their implants.

Thus, hormone implantation studies have shown that local increases of hormone concentrations in specific neural structures are stimuli adequate to trigger patterns of directed behavior. This technique has also revealed sex hormone-sensitive cells in the tuber cinereum, where substances are probably secreted which excite the production or release of gonadotropins. Considering the results of lesion and implantation studies together, one may say that estradiol has been shown to inhibit a center in the tuberal region whose activity increases LH production in the pituitary. However, the distinction between mechanisms for gonadotropin and behavioral controls is now questionable. Sawyer's hypothesis of separate mechanisms for gonadotropin regulation and mating responses in different parts of the hypothalamus (Sawyer, 1960) meets with difficulty in studies on female rats, for the experiments of Lisk (1962a) and Clark (1942) revealed the existence of an anterior hypothalamic mechanism for mating responses, and the region concerning regulation of gonadotropins extends into the same area (Flerko and Szentagothai, 1957).

AUTORADIOGRAPHIC STUDY OF SEX HORMONES

Experiments using hormone implants can locate possible sites of hormone effects but cannot prove the hypothesis of hormonal feedback because, for that purpose, it must be shown that hormones from the blood stream arrive at the hypothetical site of action and are taken up there. Moreover, it would not be feasible to explore the brain exhaustively with implants in order to be certain that all sites of action had been found. The availability of radioactively labeled sex hormones now allows microscopic *and* exhaustive survey of the brain for sites of hormone uptake with autoradiographic techniques. Thorough and sensitive assays for estrogens in body tissues, including the brain, have been performed using biochemical methods (von Tschopp, 1946) and detection of tracers in tissue homogenates (Albert, Heard, Leblond, and Saffran, 1949), but these techniques do not afford the spatial resolution available with autoradiography.

Michael (1962) began using autoradiography with diethylstilbestrol-C^{14} dibutyrate in conjunction with the method of implantation. Radioactive implants were removed from successful locations and the tissue was prepared by autoradiographic procedures. In the developed autoradiograms blackening was found in the immediate neighborhood of the implant, falling off sharply within two or three hundred micra. Beyond the zone of radiation damage, but still in densely blackened regions, Michael found individual cells which were associated with markedly increased grain counts. He concluded that these cells are neurons which selectively take up estrogens and which could mediate the effect of estrogens on mating in ovariectomized cats. However, because of the artificial introduction of the hormone to the site of action, these data represent only a partial proof that estrogen initiates mating behavior at that site under physiological conditions. Moreover, many alternative hypotheses besides selective and functionally significant affinity for estrogens could be adduced to predict that some cells would take up the chemical more than others.

In subsequent work Michael has investigated the problem of the entry of estrogens into the brain by subcutaneously injecting hexoestrol-H^3 of high specific activity into ovariectomized cats (Glascock and Michael, 1962). Frozen brain sections were prepared for autoradiography by dipping in bulk emulsion, and other tissues were subjected to combustion and gas analysis. Preliminary reports of the results state that hexoestrol accumulated in bilaterally symmetric locations in areas involving the midline hypothalamus, the preoptic region, and the septal area. The time course of uptake in these areas followed that of classical target structures, the uterus and vagina, with peaks about five hours after injection. Descriptions of the sites of uptake in the brain have not yet been reported in detail. One notes, however, that each of the three brain structures mentioned has been implicated in sexual functions by other experiments: the midline hypothalamus is associated with gonadotropin regulation (Flerko and Szentagothai, 1957; Lisk, 1960, 1962a), the preoptic area with sensitivity to testosterone in rats (Fisher, 1956), and the lateral septal area with rates of self-stimulation dependent upon androgen levels (Olds, 1958). Indeed, this autoradiographic evidence, in conjunction with the results of anterior hypothalamic lesions in female cats (Sawyer and Robison, 1956) suggests that the negative results in the preoptic area in Harris, Michael, and Scott's implantation study (1958) would be reversed by more extensive exploration in that region.

For more than a year, under the direction of Dr. Joseph Altman, I have been working on a pilot study of estradiol-17B-H^3 uptake in the adult female rat.[1] Animals that showed regular estrus cycles and responded in the classical manner to ovariectomy and subsequent progesterone injection with estrogen priming were injected subcutaneously with 2 mc. of estradiol-17B-6,7-H^3 in sesame oil (specific activity, 41.3 curies/mM). The rats were sacrificed two or eight hours after injection by cardiac perfusion with 10 percent neutral formalin. The brains and a variety of other organs were fixed in formalin and embedded in water-soluble Carbowax, and sections were cut at 6 micra. The autoradiograms, prepared by dipping the slides in Kodak NTB-3 nuclear emulsion, were exposed for thirteen weeks. Preliminary evaluation of a series of autoradiograms suggests that estradiol is taken up by a number of structures in the diencephalon and rhinencephalon, but the most reliable results have been found in the hippocampus in patches of granule cells of the dentate gyrus and pyramidal cells of Ammon's horn (Fig. 1), and in the prepyriform cortex overlying the olfactory tract. There are also consistently high grain counts in the basal ventromedial nucleus of the hypothalamus, not always associated directly with the somata of neurons, but with regions around the neurons. Interpretation of these last data, as with all of our Carbowax material, is complicated by the relatively poor histological quality of the sections and by an artifact, possibly

[1] This investigation was supported by a grant from the U.S. Atomic Energy Commission to Professor Altman and by supplementary aid received from the John A. Hartford Foundation. My thanks are due to Mrs. Elizabeth Altman, with whom I developed our histological procedures.

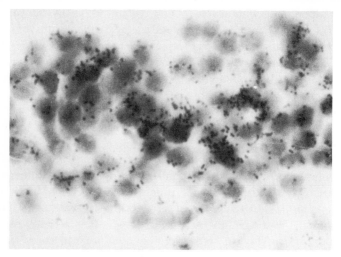

Figure 1. Labeled granule cells in the dentate gyrus of the hippocampus. Magnification: 1170X.

leaching, which prevents our getting the consistently high
resolution expected in tritium autoradiography.

Altman and Das (1964) have followed almost identical procedures in studying the uptake of tritiated testosterone
in the adult male rat. Two weeks after castration pairs of male
rats were injected subcutaneously with 2 mc. of testosterone-
1,2-H^3 in ethanol and sacrificed two or eight hours after injection. Subsequent treatment of the tissues was identical
with that of tritiated estradiol. The most reliable result which
can be reported now is that in the hippocampus the granule
cells of the dentate gyrus and pyramidal cells of Ammon's
horn bind the radioactive testosterone, although uptake in
some other structures, for instance some hypothalamic nuclei,
has not been ruled out.

If the apparent uptake of estradiol and testosterone by
these structures can be replicated, perhaps the most surprising result would be the binding of those hormones by the
hippocampus. Many studies now link the hypothalamus to
sexual functions, and the dependence of the rat on olfactory
stimuli might rationalize uptake in the prepyriform cortex,

but the role of the hippocampus in reproductive behavior has heretofore been implicated by relatively few lesion and stimulation studies. Partial ablations of the hippocampus have been shown to cause an increased frequency of mounting in male rats (Kim, 1960a), to disrupt normal cycling in female rats (Riss, Burstein, and Johnson, 1963), and to degrade nest-building (Kim, 1960b). Electrically stimulating various regions of the forebrain, MacLean and Ploog (1962) found that many sites effective in causing penile erection coincided with the anatomical distribution of the hippocampal projections and that changes in the genital response were associated with hippocampal afterdischarges in the squirrel monkey.

Present studies in Dr. Altman's laboratory are directed toward improving the Carbowax technique of embedding and developing an alternative method with frozen sections, to improve upon these pilot studies with labeled estradiol and testosterone.

SUMMARY

Two new techniques, autoradiography and direct implantation of hormones into the brain, have been used to study sites of sex hormone action, mechanisms of hormonal feedback, and induction of mating behavior in castrated animals. The principal result of these studies has been to clarify the roles of specific hypothalamic structures in the regulation of reproduction.

REFERENCES

ALBERT, S., HEARD, R. D. H., LEBLOND, C. P., and SAFFRAN, J. 1949 The distribution and metabolism of iodo-α-estradiol labeled with radioactive iodine. *J. biol. Chemistry* 177, 247–266.

ALTMAN, J. A., and DAS, G.   1964 Autoradiographic and histological evidence of postnatal hippocampal neurogenesis in rats. *J. comp. Neurol.*, in press.

CLARK, G.   1942 Sexual behavior in rats with lesions in the anterior hypothalamus. *Amer. J. Physiol. 137*, 746–749.

DAVIDSON, J. M., and SAWYER, C. H.   1961 Evidence for an hypothalamic focus of inhibition of gonadotropin by androgen in the male. *Proc. Soc. exper. Biol. Med. 107*, 4–7.

232   PFAFF

DEY, F. L.   1943   Evidence of hypothalamic control of hypophyseal gonadotropic functions in the female guinea pig. *Endocrinology 33*, 75–82.

EDSTRÖM, J-E.   1957   Effect of increased motor activity on the dimensions and staining properties of the neuron soma. *J. comp. Neurol. 107*, 295–304.

EVERETT, J. W.   1956   Functional corpora lutea maintained for months by autografts of rat hypophysis. *Endocrinology 58*, 786–796.

FISHER, A. E.   1956   Maternal and sexual behavior induced by intracranial chemical stimulation. *Science 124*, 228–229.

FLERKO, B.   1957   The effect of hypothalamic lesions of the inhibition of luteinization indirectly produced by estrogen. *Endokrinologie 34*, 202–208.

FLERKO, B.   1963   The central nervous system and the secretion and release of luteinizing hormone and follicle stimulating hormone. In A. V. Nalbandov (Ed.) *Advances in neuroendocrinology.* Urbana: University of Illinois Press.

FLERKO, B., and SZENTAGOTHAI, J.   1957   Oestrogen sensitive nervous structures in the hypothalamus. *Acta endocrinol. 26*, 121–127.

GLASCOCK, R. F., and MICHAEL, R. P.   1962   The localization of oestrogen in a neurological system in the brain of the female cat. *J. Physiol. 163*, 38–39.

HARRIS, G. W.   1955   *Neural control of the pituitary gland.* London: E. Arnold.

HARRIS, G. W.   1962   The development of neuroendocrinology. In J. D. French (Ed.), *Frontiers in brain research.* New York: Columbia Univ. Press.

HARRIS, G. W., MICHAEL, R. P., and SCOTT, P. P.   1958   Neurological site of action of stilboestrol in eliciting sexual behavior. In G. E. W. Wolstenholme and C. M. O'Connor (Eds.), *Ciba Foundation symposium on the neurological basis of behavior.* Boston: Little, Brown.

IFFT, J. D.   1962   Evidence of gonadotropic activity of the hypothalamic arcuate nucleus in the female rat. *Anat. Rec. 142*, 1–8.

KANEMATSU, S., and SAWYER, C. H.   1963a   Effects of hypothalamic estrogen implants on pituitary LH and prolactin in rabbits. *Amer. J. Physiol. 205*, 1073–1076.

KANEMATSU, S., and SAWYER, C. H.   1963b   Effects of intrahypothalamic and intrahypophyseal estrogen implants on pituitary prolactin and lactation in the rabbit. *Endocrinology 72*, 243–252.

KIM, C.   1960a   Sexual activity of male rats following ablation of hippocampus. *J. comp. physiol. Psychol. 53*, 553–557.

KIM, C.   1960b   Nest building, general activity and salt preference of rats following hippocampal ablation. *J. comp. physiol.
Psychol. 53,* 11–16.

KNIGGE, K. M.   1962   Gonadotropic activity of neonatal pituitary glands implanted in the rat brain. *Amer. J. Physiol. 202,*
387–391.

KOMISARUK, B.   1964   Personal communication.

LEHRMAN, D. S., and WORTIS, R. P.   1960   Previous breeding
experience and hormone-induced incubation behavior in the
ring dove. *Science 132,* 1667–1668.

LEVEQUE, T. F.   1953   Changes in the neurosecretory cells of the
rat hypothalamus following ingestion of sodium chloride. *Anat.
Rec. 117,* 741–757.

LISK, R. D.   1960   Estrogen-sensitive centers in the hypothalamus of the rat. *J. exper. Zool. 145,* 197–205.

LISK, R. D.   1962a   Testosterone-sensitive centers in the hypothalamus of the rat. *Acta endocrinol. 41,* 195–204.

LISK, R. D.   1962b   Inhibition of castration cell formation in the
pituitary of the spayed rat by estradiol implants in the arcuate
nucleus. *Amer. Zoologist 2,* 193.

LISK, R. D.   1962c   Diencephalic placement of estradiol and
sexual receptivity in the female rat. *Amer. J. Physiol. 203,*
493–496.

LISK, R. D.   1963a   Maintenance of normal pituitary weight and
cytology in the spayed rat following estradiol implants in the
arcuate nucleus. *Anat. Rec. 146,* 281–286.

LISK, R. D.   1963b   Estradiol: evidence for its direct effect on
hypothalamic neurons. *Science 139,* 223–224.

MACLEAN, P. D., and PLOOG, D. W.   1962   Cerebral representation of penile erection. *J. Neurophysiol. 25,* 29–55.

MEYER, R. K., LEONARD, S. L., HISAW, F. L., and MARTIN, S. J.
1932   The influence of oestrin on the gonad-stimulating complex of the anterior pituitary of castrated male and female rats.
Endocrinology 16, 655–665.

MICHAEL, R. P.   1961   An investigation of the sensitivity of cir-
cumscribed neurological areas to hormonal stimulation by
means of the application of oestrogens directly to the brain
of the cat. In S. S. Kety and J. Elkes (Eds.), *Regional neuro-
chemistry.* London: Pergamon Press.

MICHAEL, R. P.   1962   Estrogen-sensitive neurons and sexual behavior in female cats. *Science 136,* 322–323.

MOORE, C. R., and PRICE, D.   1932   Gonadal hormone functions,
and the reciprocal influence between gonads and hypophysis
with its bearing on the problem of sex hormone antagonism.
Amer. J. Anat. 50, 13–20.

OLDS, J.   1958   Effect of hunger and male sex hormone on self-stimulation in the brain. *J. comp. physiol. Psychol. 51*, 321–324.

RAMIREZ, V. D., ABRAMS, R. M., and McCANN, S. M.   1963 Effect of estrogen implants in the hypothalamic-hypophyseal region on the secretion of LH in the rat. *Federation Proc. 22*, 506.

REYNOLDS, R. W.   1963 Ventromedial hypothalamic lesions without hyperphagia. *Amer. J. Physiol. 204*, 60–62.

RISS, W., BURSTEIN, S. D., and JOHNSON, R. W.   1963 Hippocampal or pyriform lobe damage in infancy and endocrine development of rats. *Amer. J. Physiol. 204*, 861–866.

SAWYER, C. H.   1960 Reproductive behavior. In J. Field, H. W. Magoun, and V. E. Hall (Eds.), *Handbook of physiology: Neurophysiology II*. Washington, D.C.: American Physiological Society.

SAWYER, C. H., and ROBISON, B.   1956 Separate hypothalamic areas controlling pituitary gonadotropin function and mating behavior in female cats and rabbits. *J. clin. Endocrinol. 16*, 914–915.

TALEISNIK, S., and McCANN, S. M.   1961 Effects of hypothalamic lesions on the secretion and storage of hypophyseal luteinizing hormone. *Endocrinology 68*, 263–272.

TSCHOPP, E.   1946 Wirksamkeit, Organkonzentration und Ausscheidung der 7-Methyl-bisdehydro-doisynolsäure. *Helvetica physiol. pharmacolog. Acta 4*, 401–410.

VAUGHAN, E., and FISHER, A. E.   1962 Male sexual behavior induced by intracranial electrical stimulation. *Science 137*, 758–759.

GLOSSARY

Ammon's horn (Ammon, a ram-headed god of the Egyptians): the hippocampus

Amplitude activity: changes in the strength or amplitude of waves, such as electrical waves registered by the EEG (electro-encephalogram)

Amygdala: a structure of the old cortex or limbic system of the brain (see Figure 2, Chapter 10)

Androgen: male sex hormone

    endogenous a.: made by the body

    exogenous a.: given by mouth or injection; introduced from without

Anestrous: without estrus, referring to an animal or species that does not have periods of coming into heat

Anlage (pl., anlagen): in embryology, the initial element or structure that develops and differentiates into a more complex structure

Anovulatory: without ovulation

Antecubital fossae: the triangular hollows on the forearm in front of the elbow joint

Archistriatum: a structure of the brain in lower species corresponding to the amygdala in mammals

Areola (pl., areolae): on the breast, the ring of colored tissue surrounding the nipple

Assigned sex: the sex declared officially and socially, as on the birth certificate, and in which the child is thenceforth reared

Automanipulative: manipulated by oneself, without a partner

Autoradiograph: a type of photograph, resembling an X-ray, in which a very thin slice of tissue is developed as if it were a photographic film; radioactive material that has found its way into any of the cells shows up as darkly colored

Autosomal inheritance

   sex-limited type: an hereditary trait may be carried on a gene of an autosome of either sex, but be able to express itself in only one sex, e.g., milk production

   sex-influenced type: as above, except that the trait expresses itself more strongly or often in one sex than the other

Autosome: a chromosome that is not one of the sex (X or Y) chromosomes

Axillary: pertaining to the axilla or armpit

Axon: the part of a nerve cell, usually long and threadlike, that conducts impulses away from the cell body to the junction with another cell

Bartholin's glands: two small reddish-yellow bodies, one on either side of the vaginal orifice

Blood-brain barrier: the supposed barrier that prevents substances circulating in the bloodstream in the brain from passing through cell walls to have a direct effect on neural tissue

Bulbus vestibuli: two masses of erectile tissue situated one on either side of the vaginal orifice and joined together by a pars intermedia

C^{14}: a radioactive isotope of carbon

Canula: a small tube inserted into body tissue through which fluid may be passed

Cardiac perfusion: a fluid, such as a dye or poison, is introduced into the heart and is thus spread throughout the veins and arteries

Caudal (*cauda,* tail): the tail end as opposed to the front or rostral end of the body (see rostral)

Cavernosum (pl., cavernosa): full of hollows, spongy; as the corpora cavernosa of the penis or clitoris

Central nervous system mechanism: a stimulus, such as light, activates the central nervous system, which then activates another bodily system—the glandular system, for example, as when changes in the length of daylight activate the pituitary gland and regulate the breeding cycle

Cerebral cortex: the outside layer of the brain, formed into two hemispheres, left and right

Cerebral excitant: a drug that excites or activates the nerve cells of the cerebral cortex

Cervix: the neck or opening of the uterus into the vaginal canal

Chelating agent (*chela,* claw): in chemistry, a substance that traps certain molecular particles and prevents them from combining with other particles

Chromosomal sex: genetic sex as revealed by the chromosome count, which is 46,XX in females and 46,XY in males; chromosomal sex does not always agree with other sex variables, and in various abnormal conditions a sex chromosome may be missing or duplicated

Chromosomes: the threadlike structures in the nucleus of cells along which are arranged the genes, the heredity-carrying bodies. In man there are 22 pairs of autosomes and 1 pair (XX in the female and XY in the male) of sex chromosomes

Cingulate gyrus: a structure in the old cortex or limbic system (see Figures 2 and 4, Chapter 10)

Circulus venosus of Haller (*halleri*): circle of veins beneath the areola of the nipple

Clitoris (pl., clitorides, pronounced cli-tor-eé-diz): see Figure 2, Chapter 1

CNS: central nervous system, that is the brain, spinal cord, and sensory and motor peripheral nerves

Coition: coitus; sexual intercourse or copulation

Colposcope: an instrument for the visual examination of the vagina and cervix; a vaginal speculum

Corpus (pl., corpora): body; the body of an organ as opposed to its extremities and appendages

Corpus luteum (pl., corpora lutea): "yellow body"; a yellow mass in the ovary formed from the graafian follicle after the egg is released. It produces progesterone, the pregnancy hormone, and grows and lasts for several months if the egg is fertilized and pregnancy occurs

Cowper's glands: two internal glands near the base of the penis that have ducts opening into the bulbous urethra. They secrete a sticky, lubricant material

CPS: cycles per second

Critical period: a period in the life history that is particularly important for some or other aspect of growth and maturation; organs or functions prevented from developing properly during their critical period remain deformed or defective; after the critical period, adverse influences and interferences are more easily resisted

Cross-dressing: dressing in the clothes of the opposite sex, particularly as the result of a compulsion that cannot be resisted and that is associated with sexual, erotic feeling: cross-dressing is also known as transvestism

Crus (pl., crura): the leg, stalk, or trunk of a structure, as the two legs of the clitoris that separate and join to the pubic arch

Curie: a standard unit for measuring the amount of radioactivity; it is the amount of radium emanation in a closed container in radioactive equilibrium with a gram of radium

Cystourethrocele: prolapse of the female urethra and bladder

Dentate: saw-edged or tooth-edged

Dentate gyrus: a serrated, banded structure of the hippocampus

Diencephalon: the midbrain, between the brainstem and the limbic and neocortical structures; it comprises the thalamus and other structures that MacLean has termed the old reptilian brain (see Chapter 10)

Diestrus: a short period of sexual quiescence in the females of estrous species before they come into heat (estrus)

Diethylstilbestrol: a synthetic drug that acts as a female sex hormone; structural variants include the dipropionate, dilaurate, and dibutyrate esters, and C^{14}-diethylstilbestrol dibutyrate, the radioactive form used only for special investigative procedures

Ducti deferentes: the ducts leading from the testicles to the urethra of the penis

Edema (adj., edematous): the presence of excess fluid in the intercellular tissue spaces of the body

Ego identity: the sameness, unity, and persistence of one's individuality, in greater or lesser degree, especially as it is experienced in self-awareness and behavior

Electroencephalogram (EEG): the ink tracing of wave patterns generated by electrical activity in the brain and recorded electromechanically

Electrophysiological activity: normal electrical activity in the body's tissues, particularly the nervous system

Embryonic sexual differentiation:
  A. Internal (see Figure 1, Chapter 1)
  B. External (see Figure 2, Chapter 1)

Endocrine: pertaining to the ductless or hormone-secreting glands

Endometrium: the mucous membrane that lines the cavity of the uterus

Enzyme: an organic compound that speeds and facilitates chemical changes in another substance, often in a single specific substance; enzymes are important regulators of basic body chemistry

Epididymis: an oblong body attached to the upper part of each testicle containing a twisted length of the duct (ductus or vas deferens) that joins the testicle with the urethra

Epigastrium: the upper middle portion of the abdomen, over or in front of the stomach

Epileptogenic foci: limited areas of the brain, scarred or otherwise injured, that become the focal starting points of epileptic seizures. Surgical removal of the defective area may sometimes abolish seizures

Epithelial cells: cells of the skin and mucous membrane; glandular or secretory cells are specialized epithelial cells, as are neuroepithelial cells

Erogenous zones: parts of the body in which sexual sensations and feelings can be aroused or induced

Eroticism: sexual arousal and response in personal experience

Erythema (adj., erythematous): redness of the skin due to congestion of the capillaries with blood

Ester: in chemistry, a structural variant of a compound; it is formed by the combination of an acid and an alcohol

Estradiol: a crystalline estrogenic steroid, a form of female sex hormone; structural variants include estradiol benzoate and tritiated estradiol (e.g., estradiol-17B-H^3 and estradiol-17B-6, 7-H^3), which is radioactive and used only for special investigative procedures

Estrogen: female sex hormone

    endogenous e.: made by the body

    exogenous e.: given by mouth or injected; introduced from without

Estrus: the phenomenon of being in heat, as found in the sexual cycle of the females of some species

Ethnography: ethnology; the study of organized social groups (ethnic groups), their communities and ways of life

External morphologic sex: the organs of the reproductive anatomy that are visible (see Figure 2, Chapter 1)

False pelvis: the part of the pelvis above the iliopectineal line, the lower part being the true pelvis

Feedback: a servomechanism or control system in which a signal produces a response that then itself becomes a signal to produce an alteration of the initial signal

Feedback, hormonal: see above; an example is that pituitary gonadotropins release gonadal sex hormones which then signal the pituitary to diminish the production of gonadotropin

F_1 hybrids: in breeding and hybridizing experiments, the parental generation is technically known as the P_1, the first generation following a cross as the F_1 (first filial) generation, the second as the F_2, and so on

Fellatio: stimulation of the penis by taking it in the mouth, possibly to the point of orgasm

Fledgling: a young bird that has just acquired the feathers necessary for flight

Follicles, cystic: ovarian follicles that enlarge into fluid-filled cysts

Folliculogenesis: the formation of ovarian (graafian) follicles on the ovary

Formalin: a trade name for formaldehyde, a preservative and disinfectant, and a fixing agent in histologic work

Fornix (pl., fornices): the vault or upper part of the vagina; also a bundle of nerve fibers in the midbrain (see Figure 2, Chapter 10)

Fourchette: the fold of mucous membrane at the posterior junction of the labia majora

FSH: follicle stimulating hormone; it is produced by the pituitary gland and stimulates the formation of the ovarian follicle on the ovary, and the production of estrogen; when the follicle ripens, luteinizing hormone takes over, and the progestinic phase of the menstrual cycle appears

Gender identity: the sameness, unity, and persistence of one's individuality as male or female (or ambivalent), in greater or lesser degree, especially as it is experienced in self-awareness and behavior; gender identity is the private experience of gender role, and gender role is the public expression of gender identity

Gender role: everything that a person says and does, to indicate to others or to the self the degree that one is male or female or ambivalent; it includes but is not restricted to sexual arousal and response; gender role is the public expression of gender identity, and gender identity is the private experience of gender role

Genital tubercle: see Figure 1, Chapter 1

Genotype: the genetic make-up of an individual or group, as determined by the genes and chromosomes; the genotype shows itself only in interaction with its environment, the observable product being the phenotype

Glans (pl., glandes, pronounced glán-deez): the head of the penis or clitoris

Gonadal dysgenesis: imperfect formation or genesis of the gonads or sex glands; there is a syndrome of gonadal dysgenesis in phenotypic females also known as Turner's syndrome

Gonadal sex: sexual status as indicated by the ovarian or testicular structure of the gonads or sex glands; gonadal sex does not always agree with other sex variables

Gonadectomy: removal of the gonads, or castration

Gonadotropin, gonadotrophin: a hormone released by the pituitary gland (hypophysis) which stimulates gonadal (sex gland) function. The gonadotropins are follicle stimulating hormone (FSH); luteotropin (LTH), which is the same as prolactin; and luteinizing hormone (LH), which is the same as interstitial cell stimulating hormone (ICSH)

Graafian follicle: the follicle on the ovary in which the egg grows; after the egg is released, the graafian follicle becomes the corpus luteum

Grooming: a type of behavior observed in apes and monkeys, having both social and sexual significance, in which one animal strokes, picks, and combs through its fingers the hair of another's coat

Gynecology: the branch of medicine that deals with woman's constitution and diseases, especially as related to the reproductive system

Gyrus: in the brain, a convolution or fold of the cerebral cortex bounded by fissures or sulci

Hermaphroditism: a congenital condition of ambiguity of the reproductive structures so that the sex of the individual is not clearly defined as exclusively male or exclusively female; the condition is named for Hermes and Aphrodite, the Greek god and goddess of love

Hermaphroditism, cryptorchid hypospadiac: undescended testes (cryptorchidism) and a penis with an open gutter in the place of a urethral tube produce ambiguity of sexual appearance in a male

Heterogenous strain: not inbred; a strain produced without selective pairing of mates in each generation

Heterosexuality: sexual attraction or practices between members of the opposite sex

Heterospecific matings: cross-breeding between different species or types

Heterotypical hormones: hormones typical of one sex given to individuals of the other sex

H^3-hexestrol: tritiated hexestrol, a radioactively labeled form of synthetic estrogen, used as a tracer or indicator in investigative studies of estrogen uptake by various cells of the body

Hexoestrol-H^3: same as H^3-hexestrol

Hippocampus: a structure of the old cortex or limbic system (see Figures 2 and 4, Chapter 10), named for its supposed curled resemblance to a sea horse

Hirsutism: excessive hairiness; especially of masculine degree and distribution in the female

Histophysiology: physiology of cells and minute cell structures, as for example, in the study of hormone-secreting cells

Homogenate (tissue): the product obtained when tissues have been homogenized in a mechanical blender

Homologous (n., homologue): having the same relative position, proportion, value, or structure as something else: as, for example, the archistriatum in lower species, which is the homologue of the amygdala in mammals

Homosexuality: sexual attraction and practices between members of the same sex

Hormonal sex: sexual status as indicated by the predominance of male or female hormone production in the body; hormonal sex controls pubertal development of the body as male or female; it does not necessarily agree with other sex variables

Hospitalism: an adverse reaction of infants to prolonged hospitalization so that they fail to thrive and do not develop psychologic normalcy, presumptively through lack of sufficient personal mothering

Ht-H rating: heterosexual–homosexual rating

Hybrid: a cross-bred animal or plant

Hyperadrenocorticism: genetically determined abnormal overactivity of the adrenal cortex as characteristic of the adrenogenital syndrome; failing to synthesize cortisone, the adrenals produce male sex hormone instead; before birth, this adrenal error produces visible hermaphroditism in girls; after birth it produces early and excessive virilization in both sexes

Hypertrophy: excessive enlargement, as of an organ or structure; the opposite of atrophy

Hypophysis: the pituitary gland

Hypophysectomy: surgical removal of the hypophysis (pituitary gland), as in the attempted treatment of breast cancer in women, or for experimental studies in animals

Hypothalamus: a structure of the midbrain or diencephalon (see Figure 2, Chapter 10); it is the part of the brain in closest proximity to the pituitary gland; its nuclei include: the anterior, arcuate, dorsolateral, lateral, paraventricular, and ventromedial

Hysterectomy: surgical removal of the uterus

I^{131}: a radioactive isotope of iodine

Inbred strains: in laboratory animals, such as mice, purebred strains obtained by inbreeding close relatives—offspring with parents, for example, or brothers with sisters

Infantile autism: a severe psychiatric disorder in infants and children characterized chiefly by severe disturbance of the ability to communicate in social interaction; such children live in their own private or autistic mental world

Infrahuman vertebrates: backboned animals lower than human beings in the evolutionary scale

Infraprimate mammals: mammals below the primates (man, apes, monkeys) in the evolutionary scale

Insertee: in homosexual relations, a partner who accepts another's penis into his mouth or anus

Insertor: in homosexual relations, a partner who puts his penis into another's mouth or anus

Instinctoid: resembling an instinct

Integument: a covering, especially the skin

Internal morphologic sex: the accessory organs of the reproductive anatomy, that is, the organs located within the body except for the ovaries or testicles; in the female they comprise chiefly the uterus and fallopian tubes and are derived from the embryonic mullerian ducts; in the male they comprise chiefly the epididymedes, vasa deferentia and the prostate and are derived from the embryonic wolffian ducts (see Figure 1, Chapter 1)

Introitus: the entrance to the vagina; the vulva

Ion: in chemistry and physics, an electrically charged atom or group of atoms; part of a compound

Ischium: the bone upon which the body rests in sitting

Isotope: in chemistry and physics, alternative forms of an element that are the same except for a difference in atomic weight; some isotopes are radioactive

Isotopic gas analysis: a method of determining whether a sample of gas contains a radioactive tracer-isotope; the gas may be obtained by burning a solid, for example an animal tissue, that has been exposed to radioactive tracer material; the radioactivity level of the gas sample is determined by electrically counting the radioactive particle disintegrations per minute (d.p.m.); from the d.p.m. level the radioactive isotope fraction of the gas sample can be calculated as an index of whether or not the tracer is present

Kinetic: of or pertaining to motion

Klüver-Bucy syndrome: a pattern of changed behavior experimentally produced in animals by surgical removal of the amygdala from the brain, and first demonstrated by H. Klüver and P. C. Bucy in the late 1930's; among other things, the syndrome includes change from aggressiveness to docility in undomesticated monkeys, indiscriminate food choice, and changes in the regulation of sexual behavior

Labeled hormone: a substance prepared to contain a radioactive isotope in its chemical structure is said to be labeled or tagged with radioactivity

Labia majora and minora: see Figure 2, Chapter 1

Labioscrotal folds: see Figure 2, Chapter 1

Larva: the immature, wingless, and often wormlike form in which certain insects hatch from the egg and in which they remain until further developmental changes occur

Lateral ventricle: a fluid-filled space in each hemisphere of the brain, with a central part and three horns

LH: luteinizing hormone

Libido: sexual drive or urge

Limbic cortex, lobe, or system (*limbic* = forming a border around): the old cortex or paleocortex, as contrasted with the neocortex of the brain (see Figures 2 and 4, Chapter 10)

Lobotomy (frontal lobotomy): a surgical treatment once favored in the treatment of some forms of chronic psychiatric illness; the frontal lobes of the cerebral cortex were disconnected from the remainder of the cortex

Lordosis: the position of arching the back and elevating the haunches so as to receive the male in intercourse, typical of most mammals

Lumen: the open interior of a tube

Luteinizing hormone (*LH*): the hormone from the anterior pituitary gland that induces release of the egg from the graafian follicle and transformation of the latter into a corpus luteum (nonfunctional); LH in the female is the same as ICSH (interstitial cell stimulating hormone) in the male

Luteotropin, luteotrophin, or luteotropic hormone (*LTH*): the hormone from the pituitary gland that in the nonpregnant woman maintains the corpus luteum for about two weeks and causes the release of progesterone from it; LTH is the same as lactogenic hormone or prolactin and is responsible for the initiation of milk production at the end of pregnancy

Macroscopic structural change: alteration of large, as compared with microscopic, structures of the body as a result, for example, of prenatal conditions or treatment

Macrosmatic: having the sense of smell strongly or acutely developed

Mammae (adj., mammary): the breasts

Mammillary bodies: a pair of small spherical masses situated in the brain in the region of the hypothalamus and near the stalk of the pituitary gland (see Figures 2 and 4, Chapter 10)

Marasmus: progressive wasting and emaciation, particularly in infants, and especially when there is no obvious or ascertainable cause

Masculine–feminine continuum: a supposed spectrum of masculinity and femininity, with the extremes at each end, like black and white, and with graduated shades of grey between

Masculine–feminine dichotomy: a supposed contrast of masculine and feminine, allowing for no overlap

Masturbation: self-stimulation of the sexual organs

Meatus: a passage or opening, as the orifice through which urine leaves the body

Median forebrain bundle: a structure of the brain joining the limbic system and the hypothalamus (see Figures 2 and 4, Chapter 10)

Micron (pl., micra or microns): a unit of length, the thousandth part of one millimeter; symbol, μ

mM: abbreviation for millimol; one thousandth part of a gram-molecule, that is, of an amount of a substance numerically equal in grams to its own molecular weight

Mons: in anatomy, an eminence, as the mons pubis; an eminence in front of the body and superior ramus of the pubic bone; the mons veneris is the female mons pubis

Morphologic sex: sexual status as indicated by the structure or form of the (a) internal and (b) external reproduction organs, which may contradict one another and/or the other sex variables

Morphology: structure

Mullerian duct system: see Figure 1, Chapter 1

Multipara (adj., multiparous): a woman who has given birth to two or more children

Muscles

   bulbocavernosus: the muscle that in the male compresses the urethra and in the female contracts the vaginal orifice and compresses the vestibular bulbs (at the vaginal entrance)

   ischiocavernosus: a muscle that assists in erection of the penis (clitoris)

   levator ani: a muscle that supports the pelvic viscera

   rectus abdominus: a muscle that supports the abdominal viscera and flexes the vertebral column

   sphincter ani externus: the external ringlike muscle that closes the anus

Mutant: the product of a mutation, that is of a change in heredity as determined by change in the genes

Neural tissue: the tissue of nerve cells

Neuron: a nerve cell and its threads (axon and dendrites)

Nonparous: not having borne a child

Nucleolus (pl., nucleoli; adj., nucleolar): a comparatively large, conspicuous, and usually rounded body found in the nucleus of most cells

Nullipara (adj., nulliparous): a woman who has never borne a child

Nymphomania: in women, compulsive and excessive pursuit of sexual encounters; the counterpart of satyriasis in men

Olfactory: pertaining to smell or the sense of smell

Olfactory tract: a band of neural fibers arising in the olfactory bulb and communicating with the frontal lobe of the cerebral cortex; it is concerned with the sense of smell

Orgasm (adj., orgasmic): intense excitement reaching a culmination or climax, as in sexual intercourse

Ornithology: the study of birds

Os: mouth or opening, as the os of the cervix; also a bone

Ovariectomy: surgical removal of the ovaries; castration

Papez theory: a theory advanced by J. W. Papez in 1937, in a paper entitled "A Proposed Mechanism of Emotion," to the effect that the hypothalamus, the anterior thalamic nuclei, the gyrus cinguli, the hippocampus, and their connections constitute a harmonious mechanism which may elaborate the functions of central emotion, as well as participate in emotional expression

Parasympathetic: a division of the autonomic nervous system (as contrasted with the CNS): the craniosacral division, comprising the ocular, bulbar, and sacral subdivisions; it functions complementary to the sympathetic division

Papillary: composed of papillae, that is small pimple- or nipple-shaped elevations, for example, goose pimples

Paraventricular lesions: lesions made, as in brain experiments, on the ventricular wall of the hypothalamus

Parity (adj., parous): the condition of a woman with respect to having borne or not borne a child or children

Patulous: expanded, open

Pectinoform: arranged like the teeth of a comb; comb-shaped

Perineum (adj., perineal): the anatomical region at the lower end of the trunk between the thighs

Phallus: the penis; the embryonic organ, the genital tubercle, that develops into either a penis or a clitoris

Phenotype: opposite of genotype; the observable product of the interaction of the genotype with its environment

Phylogenetic: characteristic of the phylogeny, race, or species as contrasted with the individual

Pituitary gland: an endocrine gland situated deep in the brain in the midline behind the eyes; the hormones of the anterior pituitary regulate many functions of the other endocrine glands of the body; the pituitary and hypophysis are the same

Plexus: a network or tangle, especially of nerves, veins or lymphatics

    p. hemorrhoidalis externus: a network of veins surrounding the lower part of the rectum

    p. pudendalis: a venous plexus lying behind the pubis and surrounding the urethra and neck of the bladder

    p. uterovaginalis: an extension of the pelvic plexus along the upper part of the vagina and cervix of the uterus

    p. vesicalis: a venous plexus on the far wall (fundus) and sides of the bladder

Polygenic: characterized by many genes acting together

Portal vessels: pertaining to the porta or "gateway," especially of the liver; the system of veins that circulates blood from the stomach and intestines through the liver

Preoptic region: a part of the hypothalamus, closely related to the pituitary gland, and situated near the transverse crossing of the optic nerves, the optic chiasma. It is believed that cells of the preoptic area secrete neurohumoral substances.

Prepyriform cortex (*pyriform,* pear-shaped): an area of the limbic cortex between the lateral olfactory gyrus and the hippocampal gyrus

Primipara (adj., primiparous): a woman bearing or having borne but one child

Progesterone: the pregnancy hormone, produced by the corpus luteum

Prolactin: the milk stimulating hormone; it is the same as luteotropin

Proprioceptive (n., proprioception): sensory feeling arising within the body itself, giving information about position and balance and their changes

Protean: assuming different shapes; changeable in form

Pruritus (adj., pruritic): itching

Pseudohermaphroditism: hermaphroditism in which the gonads are either both ovaries (female hermaphroditism) or both testes (male hermaphroditism) and not a combination of both (true hermaphroditism)

Psychosexual differentiation: the process whereby a psychosexual identity is established; in human beings differentiation is rudimentary at birth and is complexly dependent on life experience after birth

Psychosexual identity: see Gender identity

Psychosexual incongruity: incompatibility or disagreement between part or all of the gender role and identity and one or more of the physical variables of sex

Pubis: the pubic bone, that portion of the hipbone forming the front of the pelvis

Pudendum (adj., pudendal): the external sexual organs, especially of the female

Pyromania: fire-setting, especially when accompanied by sexual thrill

Ramus (pl., rami): a branch; a slender projection of bone resembling a twig or branch from a large bone, as the rami of the pubis

Rectocele: prolapse or sinking of the rectum into the vagina

Rhinencephalon: the olfactory brain, an older name for the limbic cortex

Rostral: in the brain, the part that lies nearer than some point of reference to the beak (rostrum) or nose, that is, nearer to the front end of the body as opposed to the caudal or tail end

Ruga (adj., rugal): a ridge, wringle

Sacrouterine: related to the sacrum or sacral part of the spine and to the uterus

Salpingo-oophorectomy: surgical removal of an oviduct (fallopian tube) and ovary

Scrotum (pl., scrota): in a male, the bag or pouch containing the testes

Seminal vesicles: glandular sacs, part of the male reproductive anatomy; they secrete part of the seminal fluid in which sperms are transported

Septal area or septum: part of the brain closely related to the limbic system (see Figures 2 and 4, Chapter 10)

Septum: a dividing wall or partition

Sex chromatin: a colored spot, revealed by special staining, found on the edge of the nucleus of cells obtained from females of the human and other species; it is believed to represent one of the X chromosomes; it occurs abnormally in males with the XXY syndrome, and is subject to other abnormalities

Sex variables: 1. chromosomal sex; 2. gonadal sex; 3. hormonal sex; 4. internal morphologic sex; 5. external morphologic sex; 6. assigned sex and rearing; 7. gender role and identity

Sexual differentiation, embryonic: see Embryonic sexual differentiation

Sexually dimorphic behavior: behavior that is different in males and females and that, when observed, clearly distinguishes one sex from the other

Soma: the body (except for the germ cells), especially as contrasted with the mind

Somatosensory: pertaining to body sensations

Spastic: pertaining to or characterized by spasm, as in the muscular action of orgasm

Speculum (pl., specula): an instrument for dilating the opening of a cavity of the body in order that the interior may be more easily visible

Spermatogenesis: the process of sperm formation in the testes

Spiking activity: spike patterns observed in electroencephalographic (EEG) tracings; they are abnormal and usually indicative of convulsive seizures or epilepsy; they may be induced experimentally in studies of brain function in animals

Stilbestrol or stilboestrol: same as diethylstilbestrol

Subcutaneous implant: an object or substance, such as a hormone pellet, surgically inserted under the skin

Supraopticohypophyseal tract: a neural pathway of the hypothalamus connecting the supraoptic nucleus and the hypophysis (pituitary)

Sympathetic: a division of the autonomic nervous system (as contrasted with the CNS), namely the lumbar-thoracic division; it supplies the walls of the vascular system, the various viscera, and glands and functions complementary to the parasympathetic division

Sympatric species: different species capable of breeding together

Symphysis pubis: that part of the body, near the root of the penis or clitoris, where the pubic bones join

Syndrome: a group of signs and symptoms that occur together and characterize a disease or disorder

Synergistic action: working together; the combined effect of synergistic cooperation may be greater than the sum of the two effects taken separately

Taxonomy: classification, as of plants, animals, or diseases

Temporal primacy: occurring first or earliest

Temporal reduction: looking to the past, for example in individual development, in order to explain the present

Tenesmus: straining, as in ineffectual straining to urinate or defecate

Testosterone: a crystalline androgenic steroid, a form of male sex hormone; structural variants include testosterone propionate, testosterone sulfate, and tritiated testosterone (e.g., t.-1,2-H^3 in ethanol), which is radioactive and used only for special investigative procedures

Thyroid: the thyroid gland, an endocrine body located in the neck below the Adam's apple, which produces thyroid hormone; the dried and powdered gland of cattle and sheep, used medicationally, is also referred to as thyroid

Thyroidectomy: surgical removal of the thyroid gland

Topographical representation: in the neocortex of the brain, the patterned fitting together of the areas that regulate sensory and motor activities of the different limbs and parts of the trunk

Tritium autoradiography: autoradiography employing a tritiated (H³) radioactive isotope, e.g., tritiated estradiol

Tropic hormones: hormones, secreted by the pituitary gland, that initiate activity in other, target endocrine glands, e.g. gonadotropin, thyrotropin, adrenocorticotropin (ACTH)

Tuber cinereum: a small structure of the brain adjacent to the mammillary bodies near the pituitary gland; it is part of the hypothalamus

Tumescence: swollen or enlarged, as the sexual organs when they become engorged with blood during sexual excitement; the opposite of detumescence

Urethra: the canal through which urine from the bladder leaves the body, and in the male through which semen is ejaculated

Uterus: the womb; the female organ that holds the growing baby until birth

Vagina: the canal of the female sex organs, extending from the vulva to the cervix of the uterus, which receives the penis in sexual intercourse

Varicosity: a varicose or dilated, knotty, and tortuous part of a vein, usually of definite and limited extent

Vascular system: the system of blood vessels in the body

Vasocongestion: congestion of the blood vessels

Vasodistention: distention or dilation of blood vessels leading to increased blood supply to a part; the opposite of vasoconstriction

Venous: pertaining to the veins and their blood supply

Versene: a trade name for various synthetic amino acids and their salts which are used as chelating or sequestering agents, that is to bind divalent metallic ions, such as calcium and magnesium; Versene is used as a cleaning and degreasing agent, as a textile processing assistant, as a decontaminating agent for radioactive materials, and as a dissolving agent for proteins

Visceromotor: pertaining to movement or activity of the visceral organs

Wolffian duct system: see Figure 1, Chapter 1

INDEX OF NAMES

INDEX OF SUBJECTS

255